TAI
CHI

THE WAY TO A
HEALTHY LIFE

TAI CHI

THE WAY TO A HEALTHY LIFE

Grandmaster Gary Khor

NEW HOLLAND

First published in Australia in 2000 by
New Holland Publishers (Australia) Pty Ltd
Sydney • Auckland • London • Cape Town

14 Aquatic Drive Frenchs Forest NSW 2086 Australia
218 Lake Road Northcote Auckland New Zealand
24 Nutford Place London W1H 6DQ United Kingdom
80 McKenzie Street Cape Town 8001 South Africa

Copyright © 2000 in text: Gary Khor
Copyright © 2000 in photographs: John Maynard
Copyright © 2000 New Holland Publishers (Australia) Pty Ltd

National Library of Australia
Cataloguing-in-Publication Data:

Khor, Gary, 1947-
Tai chi, the way to a healthy life.

ISBN 1 86436574 9

1. T'ai chi ch'üan. I Title

Publishing General Manager: Jane Hazell
Publisher: Averill Chase
Publishing Manager: Anouska Good
Editors: Narelle Walford, Marie-Claire Muir
Photographer: John Maynard
Designer: Mark Thacker, Big Cat Design
Reproduction: Dot'n'Line
Printer: Times Offset, Malaysia

iv

PREFACE

I wrote this book as an introduction to the practice of Tai Chi. Tai Chi will improve not only physical health and emotional balance but also provide one with an awareness and appreciation of one's environment.

Tai Chi is much more than an exercise system for building and co-ordinating muscular activity. It teaches you techniques for releasing tension and increasing vitality. It helps you to balance emotions and strengthen the functioning of the internal organs and systems. It benefits the immunological, cardiovascular, respiratory, digestive, endocrine and eliminative systems. It also tones the muscles and improves lymphatic flow and coordination. One exercise system can do all these things because its movement techniques are based on the universal principles through which Chi operates.

When the principles on which Chi operates are understood, not only do we learn the most effective way to exercise but the most effective way of carrying out all the various activities of our lives—from the way that we cook and eat our food, to the way we work, participate in relationships, paint pictures and compose music.

This is the reason why Chi plays such a central role in traditional Chinese culture. It is therefore my hope that this book will not only bring you improved health but also start you on a journey which will change the way that you see the world around you and allow you to benefit from this new understanding in many, many ways.

While this book is complete in itself, it is only complete in the sense that each single step you take is complete. Perhaps more important is that it is the first step on a journey of understanding. An understanding that will lead you to better health, better relationships and increased quality of life.

Gary Khor

Acknowledgments

The content of this book was sourced from teaching materials during my career as a Tai Chi instructor. Over the years, one of the chief contributors to the Academy's teaching manual and curriculum has been Rod Ferguson. He continues to provide important scientific insights to Khor Tai Chi.

I am indebted to David Walker for the additional material and research information. My gratitude to Sheila Boston who worked tirelessly on the book's draft and its presentation, and June Williams for proofreading.

A special credit to Narelle Walford for her magnificent editing of text and Mark Thacker for graphic design.

And finally a big thank you to all the Academy's instructors and students who helped sustain the continual growth of the Academy.

May you all enjoy good health always.

Contents

Chapter 4 Movements

Level 1

Level 2

CHAPTER 1

Introduction

What is Tai Chi?

*T*ai Chi is a recreational exercise art that has been practised by the Chinese people for over 700 years. Famous for its relaxation qualities and graceful motions, this system of gentle, flowing movements brings relaxation and health through exercising and developing the body and the mind as one.

Underneath Tai Chi's veneer of carefree softness lies a multifaceted art. Tai Chi draws its health theory from traditional Chinese medicine, which is concerned with the flow of *chi*, the vital energy that sustains life; its fundamental principles from the philosophy of the Tao (the way of nature); and its movement structure from the 'soft internal school' of Chinese martial arts.

Tai Chi's series of connected movements incorporate these three fundamental influences, and are performed in accordance with the principles set out in the *Tai Chi Ching Classics* (a collection of works that contains the essential principles and knowledge of Tai Chi).

Tai Chi as a therapeutic system

Tai Chi, as a natural therapeutic system, balances and harmonises the body's internal energies and metabolic processes.

The physical health benefits of Tai Chi are detailed in Chapter 5, Tai Chi for Life, on pages 89–90. Briefly, they include a reduction of one's stress levels, better breathing, more efficient cardiovascular and lymphatic functioning, improved posture and more. Yet the benefits of Tai Chi go far beyond the physical.

Tai Chi addresses the individual's needs holistically—mind, body and spirit are brought into harmony through exercises that engage all these aspects of being human.

Every Tai Chi movement expresses balance and stability. When things are balanced they all work together for the benefit of the whole—in this case, you.

Tai Chi's way of balance and harmony embodies 'stillness in movement'. Emptying your mind of thoughts that cause you to be unbalanced, or stressed, and finding the essence within you—the essence of who you are—will give you wholeness. When this is the foundation from which your life springs, then you will be strong.

Thus, the practice of Tai Chi is just the beginning; the balance you will gain as your body, mind and spirit work in harmony will flow over into your life.

The origins and principles of Tai Chi

To comprehend the deeper meaning behind Tai Chi, we need to understand a little of its historical background. Although modern China bears little resemblance to traditional China, many of the original philosophical foundations have been preserved in modern life. It is possible that many of these fundamental philosophies date quite far back, even to the period around 3000 BC.

Two figures in Chinese history who made a tremendous impact in terms of the philosophical approach of Tai Chi are Huang Ti (the Yellow Emperor) and Lao Tse.

Huang Ti was reputed to have lived around 2700 BC, and is attributed with writing the *Huang Ti Nei Ching, The Yellow Emperor's Classics of Internal Medicine*. This was not only the first Chinese text on health and medicine, but one of the most important: the *Nei Ching* sets out the *chi* practices which are the basis of Chinese medicine today.

The *Nei Ching* provides evidence that the theory of *chi* goes back into pre-history. It also states that *chi*, the life force, flows along defined pathways, or meridians, within the body and that this flow of energy can be affected by the way we live and the exercise we perform. This is the theory on which Tai Chi is based. One of the important aspects of Tai Chi is the manner in which it works to gain the optimal flow of *chi* within the human body. (Acupuncture is another sophisticated way of working on the flow of *chi*.) The *Nei Ching* also emphasises the importance of a balanced lifestyle and of living with due regard to the environment, the climate, one's condition and age, and to proper nutrition and sleep patterns. The observations are as valid today as they were millennia ago.

The second figure to have a profound impact on Chinese thought was Lao Tse, a Chinese philosopher born in 604 BC. Lao Tse wrote the *Tao Te Ching*, which sets out the philosophy of Taoism. The Tao can be understood (insofar as it can be understood) as the 'way of nature', the 'nature of things'. Its closest meaning in western understanding would be the 'physical laws', or the 'laws of nature'.

Huang Ti is attributed with a number of critical observations that are also espoused by the principles of Taosim. It is not unusual to find differences between various sources as to who said what, but in general these differences are irrelevant in regards to the philosophy itself.

Huang Ti's observations relating to Tao

Huang Ti's capital was built on the banks of the Yellow River, which is subject to periodic flooding. It is said that Huang Ti observed the aftermath of one of these floods and noted that when the waters lay still upon the ground they stagnated. Not only did the land look and smell offensive, but disease ravaged the human and animal populations. From this Huang Ti drew the conclusion that if people did not move they also would stagnate and become sick and diseased. He therefore formulated 'health dances', which his subjects were required to perform in order to maintain their health. These dances were not performed in order to elicit magical health but because the act of moving was, in itself, considered to be health giving.

The form and nature of these health dances has been lost to history, thus we have no way of knowing whether there was any similarity between the principles underlying these dances and those espoused in the *Tai Chi Ching Classics*.

Tao: through observing nature we learn

In our fast, modern and competitive world it would seem that rigidity and hardness are the way to power. Yet in nature it is softness and pliability that are the victors—water wears away the hardest rock, and it is the pine, not the bamboo, that falls in the storm. Thus, nature teaches us these life-sustaining traits—we only need observe the lessons.

The intuitive leap that enabled Huang Ti to connect the aftermath of a flood with the results of a sedentary human existence is simply an illustration of an even more fundamental belief that underlies Taoist philosophy—that there are general laws operating throughout nature at all levels and that human kind, as a part of nature, also reflects these laws. Thus, if lack of flow leads to stagnation in the natural world, then people, as part of that natural world, will also stagnate. Human kind was never seen as existing beyond nature, only as part of it.

It should be immediately stressed that true Taoists do not think of themselves as being swept along by forces against which they are helpless. Rather, they see themselves like birds on the air currents, or like sailors mastering their environment not by controlling the wind but by harnessing its power. Perhaps an even better analogy is the surfer, who reads and adapts to the waves—proving successful when surfer and wave are as one.

Tai Chi is an art, like flying, sailing or surfing, but instead of using currents of air or water, the practitioner uses the currents of *chi* that flow within the body. The practitioner does not control or direct, but he or she does master. The comprehension of *chi* and its pathways comes from a oneness with nature that arises from being truly aware of nature.

Books such as the *Tao Te Ching* provide insight into the ways nature works, ways that become apparent only after long observation. Awareness, however, is more than intellectual understanding—it implies a connection at the gut level. Read as many books as you like about flying, sailing and surfing, you will never be a flyer, sailor or surfer until you have got out there and, through experience, understood the element with which you are working. It is the same with Tai Chi.

The creation of Tai Chi

The creation of Tai Chi was the culmination of around 4000 years of development in Chinese philosophy, health practices and martial arts. A brief look at the various disciplines and corresponding philosophies that have blended together to form the Tai Chi art provides a fuller understanding of its depths. This understanding will allow you to reap greater enjoyment and increased health benefits from your practice of Tai Chi.

The Tao Yin era

The first actual record of Chinese exercises comes to us from the Western Han dynasty (206 BC–AD 9). The Han dynasty continued on after a brief hiatus of 16 years to AD 220; the time before this hiatus being known as the Western Han, the time after, the Eastern. A silk scroll found in a tomb depicted exercises known as Tao Yin (literally, Tao-getting exercises). These exercises were aimed specifically at working on the *chi*, which underlies all of the body's systems, and were practised in order to increase health.

The Chinese had, in fact, identified a concept known as Zhang Fu, which focuses on the health of the internal organs. *Zhang* refers to the 'solid' organs—lungs, spleen, heart, kidneys, pericardium and liver— which produce and store energy in order to nourish the whole body. *Fu* refers to the 'hollow' organs—large intestine, stomach, small intestine, bladder, triple heater (according to traditional Chinese medicine, the organ that controls *chi* functioning) and gall bladder—which regulate and transform energy within the body.

The 'pericardium' and 'triple heater' meridians cannot be directly related to specific internal organs. The pericardium meridian is indirectly related to the heart in that its function is to protect the heart against physical shock and emotional stress. The 'triple heater' meridian is even more enigmatic as there is no physical structure at all that can be associated with this meridian. Western researchers tend to relate the function of this meridian to the biochemical metabolism of the body as a whole. Readers who are interested in more fully understanding the Chinese view of the somewhat complex functioning of this meridian are referred to David Tai's book *Acupuncture and Moxibustion* (Harper and Rowe, Sydney, 1987), which provides one of the most comprehensive outlines of meridian function and relationships. Meridians are much more a matter of energetic function than they are of the physical functioning of specific tissues and organs. Western and Chinese views of the body represent completely different paradigms of thought. Both can be used to cure the body in different ways, but you cannot create a hybrid theory that fully incorporates both approaches.

While it was recognised that any exercise which worked on the *chi* would have an effect on the whole body, it was also believed that exercises which directly stimulated specific organ meridians could strengthen the energy flow in that meridian. Thus, exercises were designed with this concept in mind.

Tao Yin exercises often imitated the physical movements of animals. Chuang Tse (a famous philosopher who lived in the fourth century BC) is known to have said, 'As a means to long life, spend some time like a dormant bear'. Other contemporaries of Chuang Tse recommended one to, 'Imitate the flappings of a duck, the ape's dance, the owl's fixed stare, the tiger's crouch and the pawings of a bear'.

Breathing exercises were developed to synchronise with the body movements, and each movement was performed separately. The objective was to preserve the health and harmony of the mind.

A famous doctor of the Han dynasty named Hua Toe, who lived in the second century AD, built upon the Tao Yin-type exercises by utilising mental imagery to effectively work on the emotions and psychology of the individual. Here, instead of the mind trying to assume direct control of the body, it merely established general imagery to which the subconscious could relate. Movements now gained a specific flavour, as well as direction, and included the use of both the left brain (for memory, willpower and comprehension) as well as the right brain (for imagination, creativity and emotional function).

Hua Toe can be said to have rounded out the development of Tao Yin, making it a sophisticated, therapeutic system to stimulate the organ meridians, both through movement and visualisation—a complete mind/body exercise. Tao Yin is an ideal therapeutic system for working on a specific health problem.

The Shaolin era

In the sixth century AD, a Buddhist monk called Bodhidharma (Chinese name, Ta Mo) travelled from India to China and became abbot to the Shaolin temple. Disturbed to find the monks in poor physical condition and lacking in concentration and spiritual development, Ta Mo instituted a simple health regimen, which had the effect of stimulating circulation, loosening the joints and restoring vitality. This came from a fusion of Chinese and Indian practices and also included martial arts techniques.

During Ta Mo's time at the temple, the monks gained a reputation for physical and mental discipline. Ta Mo is also credited with the introduction of the martial arts virtues of discipline, restraint, humility and respect for human life.

The Shaolin era marks the interweaving of Chinese health philosophy and practices and those of the martial arts. It may seem strange that martial arts and health theory should find themselves so closely aligned when their aims, at first glance, seem so different. However, martial arts provided the health arts with a number of things which they had been lacking, one of these being a particular awareness that went with martial arts exercises: that you needed to be able to 'read' the actions of your opponent. This lead to the development of the concept of 'listening' to energy, which really has no counterpart in the western world. Being sensitive to the flow of energy, or chi, allows one to respond correctly.

The evolution of Shaolin Chuan

Over time, the Shaolin temple style evolved the 'Five Chuan', or Five Fists: the Tiger, Leopard, Snake, Crane and Dragon chuan. Each *chuan* was performed for a specific purpose—Tiger, to strengthen the bones; Leopard, to develop the muscular system; Snake, to develop *chi*; Crane, to develop the sinews, tendons, ligaments and connective tissue; and Dragon, with its slow, soft movements, inner stillness and lightness, was performed to develop attention and spirit (*shen*) and may well have been one of the precursors of Tai Chi.

As a matter of interest, Crane Chuan is the system on which Rolfing and Postural Integration are based, and combination of the Snake and Crane styles lead to the development of the martial art of Wing Chun. The Shaolin Chuan, when exported to Korea, became Tae Kwon-Do, and when exported to Japan became Karate, Judo, Jujitsu and Aikido.

The founders of the Tai Chi form

There is much uncertainty and contradiction concerning what happened during this period between the development of the Shaolin form of the sixth century and the emergence of the Tai Chi form. However, we do know that people began to connect movements into a continuous form, including many of the movements we know today.

The person generally accepted as the founder of Tai Chi was Chang San Feng, who lived during the Sung dynasty (AD 960–1279).

There are many stories about Chang San Feng. There seems to be, however, a general agreement that as well as being a Taoist he also attended the Shaolin monastery, where he mastered the various forms of Shaolin Chuan. These forms apparently did not satisfy him, and he retired to the Wu Dang mountains to contemplate the deficiencies of the Shaolin school of martial arts. Chang San Feng was said to have struggled for years to reconcile the external martial arts forms of the Shaolin with the 'way of nature' taught in Taoist philosophy. It is reputed that Chang San Feng had a dream about a fight between a snake and a crane (some sources replace the crane with a magpie)—the snake bending and coiling to escape the striking beak, then using the energy of its coils to strike back at the crane; the crane using its wings to deflect the snake's strike, together with skillful positioning of its body for attack and defence.

Exactly how Chang San Feng used the knowledge from this dream to create Tai Chi is not revealed, but it is speculated that the snake represented the internal energy, the crane the outer structure and form. The secret of Tai Chi was to blend these two aspects into one. Chang San Feng is also credited with introducing the Chi Kung (*chi* meaning energy, and *kung* meaning skill) breathing techniques used in Tai Chi, which focused on maximising the flow of *chi* throughout the body.

Since Tai Chi-like forms were in existence prior to Chang San Feng's influence, it is interesting that the Chinese should see his role in the development of Tai Chi as being so important. Most attribute this to the fact that Chang San Feng integrated the sequence of movements with the Five Elements Theory (wood, fire, water, earth and metal; in Tai Chi they represent the five directions—forward, backward, leftward, rightward and centre) and the I Ching Theory (the *Book of Changes*; a text that relates the concept of constant change as the interaction of two complementary forces—*yin* and *yang*; see pages 12–13 for further details), and thus made Tai Chi more than a martial art. Chang San Feng developed Tai Chi into a system of great personal benefit, extending beyond defence or even physical health—turning it into a series of exercises that could develop a person mentally, spiritually and emotionally.

The martial schools era

This is a distinctive era (from the 16th to the 20th century) when the practice of Tai Chi moved away from the reclusive Taoists and into the hands of martial arts families. While these families contributed immensely to the arts, they also had a somewhat different approach—Tai Chi was now a matter of livelihood. The schools competed with each other in terms of who and how many they could beat, and new techniques were kept secret—the focus on health and spiritual development remained, but was subordinate to the martial arts aspects.

This period, then, can tend to become simply a history of who taught whom and who invented what school. It should, however, never be forgotten that many of the contributions to the *Tai Chi Ching Classics* came from this time. It can be seen as a period of refinement and revision rather than of any startling new developments.

Tai Chi evolved further throughout this era with different masters creating their own styles and forms. This brought into existence the four main styles that we have today—Chen (the first form, of which there exists a detailed record of the movements), Yang, Wu and Sun. The Yang style was modernised in the 1920s into its current form by taking out many of the faster movements and combining similar postures. It is the most popular Tai Chi form. Khor-style Tai Chi is a refinement of it.

The modern era

With the ascension of the communist government in China during the 1940s and early 1950s, Tai Chi's usage began to branch out and the influence of the martial arts and of the Taoists was reduced. At the end of the revolution, the government simply could not afford a western-style medical system, besides which, the Chinese had always been more interested in prevention than cure. Tai Chi was thus promoted widely throughout the country as a health exercise system—it neatly fitted requirements and reduced the need for hospital services.

During this time, Tai Chi also evolved into Wushu, a national sport to promote Chinese culture. In this context it was developed as a performance art, its emphasis on aesthetics and performance characteristics. With these developments, Tai Chi's aspects of spiritual development and improvement were, once again, pushed into the background.

Modern Chinese Tai Chi styles

The number and variety of Tai Chi schools in China meant that many forms were being evolved and taught. The Chinese government therefore decided to establish a 'national' set that could be used for competition and health promotion purposes—one that was simple to teach, simple to learn and which avoided rivalry between different schools.

They selected four Tai Chi masters from various schools, instructing them to create one combined set by drawing on the best from the styles each master represented. The result was the Beijing 24, released in 1956, and mainly based on the Yang style. Many people found this set too short, and it was later followed by the Beijing 48, along with a 'Combined Tai Chi Chuan Routine'. Apart from in competition, these sets do not appear to have found particular favour with the Chinese people, and are seen as second best even by the masters who created them. Undoubtedly, if combined with the inner knowledge of Tai Chi they can be useful and successful forms, but (perhaps because of the competitive aspect) their focus is more on outward appearance and presentation.

The post-revolution era also inspired much migration, which dramatically increased the exposure of Tai Chi and other Chinese cultural practices to the rest of the world. Tai Chi appealed to the New Age movement, where its spiritual and philosophical aspects were emphasised to the exclusion of all others, as well as becoming popular as an alternative to the overly exertive and competitive exercises then available.

Tai Chi is now taught for many different reasons. This has caused some concern but it shouldn't. All aspects of Tai Chi should be explored and, provided the *Tai Chi Ching Classics* are adhered to, nothing will be lost. As Lao Tse noted, 'That which is stiff and hard is dead'. Tai Chi is living; it will continue to grow and develop.

Learning Tai Chi

Learning the Tai Chi art can be divided into three distinct stages, according to the principles you are seeking to implement in your practice of the Tai Chi movements:

1. Gentle relaxation—involving the gentle stretching and rhythmic movement of the body, as well as imagery and natural breathing.
2. Health reinforcement—involving body alignment, stretching, weight

transfer (loading), increased circulation, mental focus and internal/external coordination (balance).

3. Application—involving an awareness of Tai Chi's philosophical principles, and its use in stress management and in everyday living as well as self-defence applications.

Yin/Yang Theory and Tai Chi

Some important Taoist theories have already been briefly mentioned—Five Elements Theory, Meridian Theory, I Ching Theory. Although important concepts, it is certainly not necessary to have an understanding of them at this stage—their benefits either work internally or have been incorporated externally, such as in the shape or direction of the movements. However, one important theory of which you need to be aware is that of *yin* and *yang*.

Like most Taoist theories, that of *yin* and *yang* is outwardly simple but inwardly sophisticated. Its basic precept is that *yin* and *yang* represent the two mutually complementary polarities existing in nature, and that they express all change and all relationships. This theory is illustrated by a diagram called the Tai Chi Tu, which, simply put, outlines life's continual balancing act.

Figure 1: Yin *and* yang *as shown in the Tai Chi Tu*

The outside circle represents the universe and everything in it. The *yin/yang* polarities are enclosed within—each depicted as a fish-like shape, going in a continually circular direction. Each polarity contains within it a small circle of its opposite, which denotes its ability to change. The white area represents *yang*, the black, *yin*.

Being polarities, each represents opposites. Thus we have:

> **Yin**—darker, colder, heavier, descending, slower, more fluid
>
> **Yang**—brighter, warmer, lighter, ascending, faster, more rigid.

In Tai Chi, the main words associated with *yin* and *yang* are:

> **Yin**—empty, retreating, lower body, back
>
> **Yang**—full, advancing, upper body, front.

As Tai Chi works on balancing the body, *yin* and *yang* are fully and continually employed. This can be seen externally in the structure of the movements. Each time a step is about to be taken, the leg supporting the body is full, or *yang*; the leg making the step is empty, or *yin*. As the foot is placed and the transfer of weight commences, the potential for change comes into effect. The original supporting leg becomes less solid, as it releases its fullness, and the leg that has taken the step becomes less empty, as it begins to take on its new role of supporting leg.

A pushing hand is a *yang* hand; a resting hand waiting to take over, is a *yin* hand. An advancing movement is *yang*; but *yin* is always in the background, with the possibility of retreat.

This continual exchange and, therefore, balancing, takes place throughout the whole body, with each outward physical change having an effect elsewhere—internally, mentally, spiritually and emotionally. These balancing effects occurring throughout all levels of your being during your practice of Tai Chi produce a state of focused relaxation and calmness, that leads to wellbeing.

When you become sufficiently trained at reading your own Tai Chi, or *chi* flow, you will find that it also reflects the internal balance of energies at any point in time. You can use Tai Chi to identify energy imbalances within your body.

This awareness will help you to determine the lifestyle causes of those imbalances, and thus help you to take corrective action to eliminate the cause or, where this cannot be done, compensate for it. This aspect of Tai Chi is further outlined in Chapter 5, Tai Chi for Life.

Acupoints

The Tai Chi exercises included in Chapter 4 include instructions on visualising the location of *chi* in your body. The specific points mentioned, the acupoints, relate to meridian theory (also applied during acupuncture), and include the *lao gong*, *bai hui* and *yong quan* points on your body, and are represented in the figures below.

Figure 2: Acupoints

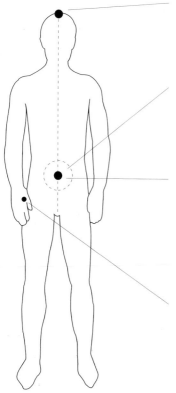

bai hui ('100 meetings point'): lifting through this point is critical both to posture and the feeling of vitality and well being

qi hai ('sea of energy'): found three finger-widths below the navel of the surface of the abdomen, this point controls the sorage of chi *in tan tien*

tan tien: the centre of gravity in the body where chi *is stored*

he gu ('valley of union'): another important point for mobilising the energy of the body

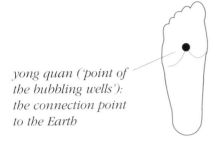

yong quan ('point of the bubbling wells'): the connection point to the Earth

lao gong: point which the heart protector meridian passes through.

Visualising *chi* in these areas during the performance of a movement stimulates the flow of *chi* in your body, thus increasing the overall health benefits of the exercise.

Khor-style Tai Chi

Khor-style Tai Chi was created as a variation of the Large Frame Yang Style which uses big, open expansive movements and forms. A product of a lifetime's study and refinement of Tai Chi, Khor-style Tai Chi adheres to the principles set out in the *Tai Chi Ching Classics*, combined with an emphasis on the health aspects. It is consistent with the latest scientific knowledge on exercise theory and movement dynamics, as well as deep studies of traditional Chinese knowledge. On its performance in China it received compliments in respect of its development of the fundamental principles of Tai Chi. The contribution of many practitioners and researchers throughout the world to this style is gratefully acknowledged.

While preserving and enhancing the inner form of Tai Chi, Khor-style Tai Chi was designed to provide an easy introduction to Tai Chi by focusing on the basic principles. It should, therefore, be viewed not only as the sequence of Tai Chi movements that goes by that name but also as a teaching methodology and philosophy that accompanies the form.

For teaching purposes, Khor-style Tai Chi is broken up into six levels, although there is no intrinsic difference between the movements in each level. Each level is, however, designed to introduce specific principles to deepen the student's appreciation and understanding of Tai Chi.

It takes at least 18 months to progress through the six levels of Khor-style Tai Chi. At the end of this time, if the student has practised diligently, he or she will have set down a firm basis for a lifetime of Tai Chi. This is, however, only the start of the journey. While many health benefits will have been obtained throughout the 18 months, the greatest benefits come when one starts to practise Tai Chi rather than learn it. Of course, the two elements of practice and learning are present throughout one's Tai Chi life, but the proportions vary.

In the first phase of Tai Chi, its 'outer' form is learned, for this is the vehicle through which the 'inner' form of Tai Chi, its principles, will be expressed. The focus is, therefore, on attaining the basic pattern and structure of the movement. Principles are taught, but are not really experienced until the student has become sufficiently confident with the sequence of movements and can perform it from memory.

In the second phase, the movements are still being perfected but emphasis has shifted to the 'feel' of Tai Chi. Here is where you truly start to 'play' Tai Chi, experimenting with different aspects of the principles.

The exercises in this book cover Levels 1 and 2 of the Khor Tai Chi Set. These exercises are sufficient to provide most of the benefits of the full set. Especially for newcomers to the Tai Chi art, Levels 1 and 2 will also provide the vital foundation of Tai Chi skills that will take you deeper into the practice of Tai Chi.

CHAPTER 2

The Five Essential Principles

*T*he principles of Khor-style Tai Chi follow those set out in the *Tai Chi Ching Classics*. They are the same as those principles used in all recognised forms of Tai Chi: relaxation, concentration, meditation, harmony and breathing. In this chapter, each principle is summarised in a succinct and easy-to-learn manner.

1. Relaxation

Be soft and yielding, exert no strength.

Relaxation is the basic principle of Tai Chi upon which everything rests. If you don't achieve a state of relaxation in your Tai Chi form, it will not succeed and its potential health benefits will be greatly minimised.

It is very important to understand that the type of relaxation you are seeking in your Tai Chi is of a 'dynamic' nature, akin to relaxed doing, rather than of a 'collapsed' nature, as might be achieved while lying on the floor. The concept of dynamic relaxation is important because of incorrect preconceptions as to the true nature of relaxation. The concept that you can best 'relax' your body while lying down is erroneous. Lying down 'rests' your muscles and lowers energy requirements, but causes significant stress on your body itself, including:

- Compression of the tissues supporting your body's weight. This causes poor blood circulation in these areas, and often results in aches and stiffness upon rising.
- Pressure of the abdominal organs against your lung diaphragm. This makes breathing harder work and reduces blood circulation to the internal organs, thus reducing your blood's capacity to supply nutrients and remove toxins.
- Lack of mobility impairs the lymphatic system, which helps defend your body against infection, as it relies on movement to circulate lymphatic fluids.
- Lack of movement also reduces the nutrient supply to the synovial membranes (which produce a lubricating liquid) of the joints and causes the development of adhesions in your body's membranes.
- The lack of muscle tone required in the limbs while lying down can cause low blood pressure problems upon rising.

Of course, your body is designed to cope with a reasonable amount of lying down, such as is found in normal sleep patterns. Excessive lying down is, however, highly deleterious to your health: doctors now encourage patients to become mobile as soon as possible, as this promotes recovery and prevents further deterioration of health.

Dynamic relaxation is achieved through Tai Chi as you exercise out any mental stresses and tensions that are held within the muscles and connective tissues of your body, and as you alternately work and rest your muscles to promote the circulation of blood and other body fluids. The relaxed and balanced movements of Tai Chi bring about a balance between your sympathetic nervous system (which prepares you for action) and your parasympathetic nervous system (which puts your body in its healing and maintenance mode). This balance between non-action and action, or *yin* and *yang*, reflects one of the fundamental principles of Tai Chi that work for your physical benefit.

Remember that Tai Chi's relaxation is holistic: relax your mind and your body. 'Mind' refers to your intellectual and emotional processes; 'body', to your posture (musculature and joints), breathing and movement.

2. Concentration

Let the mind direct each movement.
This direction means that your mind must be focused on what it's doing. Concentration does not refer to 'grit your teeth'-type determination; this would induce stress, which is in opposition to the prime principle of relaxation. It does mean, however, that your mind must be stilled and focused on your body, directing and controlling all its movements. When you achieve this, your blood circulation increases, *chi* flows freely within your body and you begin to derive Tai Chi's great health benefits.

To concentrate means to focus. When aiming a camera, we choose the subject that we want in the picture (composition) and focus the lens so that the subject is clear—the camera is no more 'strained' when focused than when unfocused. Your own focus should not be a matter of tension. Sometimes, when we take a photograph, unwanted people or animals wander in front of the subject and we wait until our view is clear again. The same should be true of your mind: if an unwanted thought strays into your mind, let it go. Do not be disturbed by it, simply ignore it.

Focus on what you are doing with your Tai Chi. If you set yourself the task of not thinking about anything but your Tai Chi, this is what you will think about, not your Tai Chi. The former brings a focused and tranquil mind, but if you focus on the latter you set yourself an impossible task. For instance, for the next five minutes try not to think of a horse. If you set yourself the goal of not thinking about something you are defeated before you start, as you must think about the subject to make sure you don't think about it. Rather, just keep turning your mind to your Tai Chi; this is what concentration means—using your will to focus—to remember the Tai Chi movements and principles and to use them.

The part of the mind that enables us to concentrate is what the Chinese call the *yi*. The *yi* can be thought of as left-brain function—willpower, intellect, logic, memory, analysis. This function combined with the right-brain meditation aspect of Tai Chi reflects the *yin/yang* principle of Tai Chi: working both hemispheres of the brain to achieve balance.

3. Meditation

Move slowly, with even tempo, describing circles in continuous flow.
When we are focused, we are aware of each movement and its nature; we 'feel' the movement and are 'at one' with it. The movement, or, more specifically, the nature of the movement, is the object of our meditation.

Simply, meditation means continuous, undistracted thought on one subject. Meditation is different to concentration. Concentration is about focusing on applying the principles and movement details; meditation is about experiencing the 'feel' and 'nature' of the movement. This involves, in Chinese terms, the application of *shen*. *Shen* can be equated to the right-brain functions—the emotions, the imagination, the creative and intuitive elements of the mind. Here, doing and experiencing are two sides of the same coin.

Body and mind each influences the other. The focus on slowness, evenness of tempo and circularity (no sudden change of direction) are important: your mind becomes tranquil and relaxed when the movements of your body are unhurried and without jerkiness. The Chinese call this mien the 'silk-like' movement of the body. Imagine drawing a thread of silk from a silkworm's cocoon: if you jerk or change direction quickly, the thread will break; if you move without jerkiness, then you can still vary the speed and direction of pull but the thread will not break.

One aspect of Tai Chi meditation is visualisation. You will notice that the names of the Tai Chi movements in Chapter 4 all provide a visual representation of the movements: Holding the Ball, Grasping the Bird's Tail, Play the Lute, and so on. Each Tai Chi movement is performed with the practitioner utilising the relevant visualistion to direct both the movement and the flow of chi throughout the body.

Though your focus is on your body, you must remain aware of the environment in which you move. Keep conscious of your surroundings as you concentrate on the visual image in your mind's eye.

4. Harmony

Move all parts of the body as one, with balance and coordination.
To harmonise means to bring into balance. When you do Tai Chi, you are employing an exercise to harmonise yourself at all levels. In Chinese terms these levels can be viewed as:

- Your *li* (or physical nature)—as expressed through your strength (which is a product of the proper functioning of your muscles, joints and ligaments), and stamina (a product of the proper functioning of your metabolic processes such as digestion, assimilation, circulation and transformation). In the martial art belief system, transformation refers to both the physical transformation of digested nutrients into bone and tissue, and the energetic transfer of *chi* into *yi* or *shen*.
- Your *chi* (or energetic nature)—as expressed by the amount and distribution of vital energy throughout your body, along with its circulation and transformation of that energy.
- Your *yi* (or mental and intellectual aspects)—the power of your will, reasoning, logic and memory, and your computative powers.
- Your *shen* (or emotional and spiritual aspects)—your sense of well being and vitality.

The objective of Tai Chi is to exercise each of the above aspects in an harmonious manner, so that all are equally developed.

5. Breathing

Breathe naturally through the nose and into the abdomen (tan tien). *With the abdomen relaxed, tranquillity will prevail.*
If your breathing is not natural, there will be stress. Breathing through

your nose, keeping your abdomen relaxed and directing your breath to the abdomen will not only increase the efficiency of your breathing but also the amount of *chi* you absorb from the air.

There is a direct link between the frequency of breathing and the predominance of the sympathetic (more breaths per minute) or the parasympathetic (less breaths per minute) nervous systems. Calming your breath helps to induce a state of tranquillity by drawing to the fore your parasympathetic nervous system.

You will notice that the injunction is to breathe naturally, not to slow your breathing through willpower. Imposing unnatural breathing rhythms on your body is not beneficial—it can cause adverse changes in your body chemistry and actually heighten tension and stress. Your in-breath is naturally activated when the levels of carbon dioxide in your blood rise beyond a certain point. Natural breathing does not mean that you cannot have any influence on how you breathe, but that you should not impose a specific number of breaths per minute on your body. The techniques detailed below will help you to find your natural breathing pattern:

- Simply 'listening' to your breathing will naturally calm and lengthen it. You should be an observer of your breath, rather than a director.
- Breathing through your nose slows the passage of air—your body will compensate for the reduction of air by lengthening and deepening your breaths.
- Focusing your mind on your abdomen and allowing it to move out on the in-breath and in on the out-breath will also help you to naturally deepen your breathing.

Correct breathing techniques are further discussed in the following chapter, Chapter 3, The Three Basic Skills.

CHAPTER 3

The Three Basic Skills

*t*he three basic skills of Tai Chi are correct weight transfer, stepping and breathing. Guidelines concerning these three principles are given in this chapter, and are fundamental to the performance of Tai Chi. Only when you have understood and practised these principles, should you commence with the Tai Chi movements given in Chapter 4.

Weight transfer

In Tai Chi the weight of your body is constantly shifting from foot to foot. The process by which you change the amount of weight carried by each foot is called weight transfer. Prior to taking a step, for example, we transfer 100 per cent of our body weight to the supporting foot. There are, however, stances where only a portion of the weight is transferred.

The principles that apply to weight transfer are described below, and are the same regardless of the amount of weight transferred. While weight transfer can appear to be a simple mechanical process, in Tai Chi it is also the expression of one of the fundamental principles that underlie the art—the Yin/Yang Theory. Weight transfer is therefore something that needs to be done with awareness and understanding.

Think of the leg that holds the weight as being the *yang* leg, and the other leg as the *yin* leg. Weight transfer, then, looks at the change from *yang* to *yin* and vice versa. The ability to feel this difference and be aware of the change is important, as this will help you increase your flow of *chi* as you mentally direct it through the movement via visualisation.

Principles of weight transfer

The following principles of weight transfer must be applied to all of your Tai Chi movements:

- The transfer of weight can only commence once both feet are in contact with the ground. Weight transfer should not happen while one foot is still suspended in the air.
- Weight should be transferred slowly and fluidly, without jerkiness.
- The movement of the knee joints must be synchronised so that the height of the body remains the same. (There can be a tendency to push the weight from the weighted leg without making a proper adjustment to the leg receiving the weight. This causes a bobbing effect that reduces stability.)
- When transferring weight, don't push your knee so far forward that it extends beyond your toes. This puts your knee at risk, as well as creating instability.
- When transferring weight, pay attention to the leg from which the weight is being transferred so that it does not straighten, and so that the knee remains facing in the same direction as the foot.

Exercises

The best way to familiarise yourself with the mechanics of weight transfer is to practise the following weight transfer techniques. Don't let the simplicity of these exercises cause you to overlook their value, and remember to use them.

Shoulder-width Stance

This is the stance from which you will commence your Tai Chi set in Chapter 4. For this basic stance your feet should be positioned shoulder-width apart and parallel, with your toes facing forwards and your weight equally distributed on both feet.

EXERCISE 1: BASIC WEIGHT TRANSFER

A Commencing from the Shoulder-width Stance, bend your knees as far as is comfortable. Keep your back straight.

B Slowly transfer your weight onto your left foot, and hold for a count of three.

C Slowly transfer weight onto right foot. Hold for a count of three.

D Repeat steps B and C six times.

EXERCISE 2: WEIGHT TRANSFER WITH BALANCE

A Commencing from the Shoulder-width Stance, bend your knees as far as is comfortable. Keep your back straight.

B Slowly transfer all your weight onto the left foot and draw in your right foot till it reaches the side of your left foot. Keeping your right foot off the ground, hold for a count of three. Make sure your knees are still bent and pointing in the same direction as your toes. Place the 'empty', or right, foot back in the Shoulder-width Stance.

C Slowly transfer your weight onto your right foot and draw in your left foot until it reaches the side of your right foot. Keeping your left foot off the ground, hold for a count of three. Make sure your knees are still bent and pointing in the same direction as your toes. Place the 'empty', or left, foot back in the Shoulder-width Stance.

D Repeat steps B and C six times.

Square Stance—left and right

To obtain a Left-foot Square Stance, place your heels together, with your left foot facing forwards and your right foot facing 90 degrees to the right. Take each foot forward in the direction of the toes, putting the heels just in front of where the toes were and adjusting the right foot so that it inclines 45 degrees towards the left foot. Transfer 70 per cent of your weight onto your left foot. Your body should be facing in the same direction as the front, or left, foot.

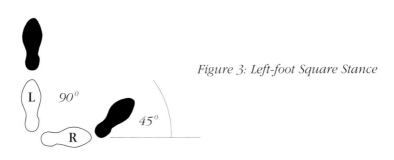

Figure 3: Left-foot Square Stance

The Right-foot Square Stance can be obtained simply by mirroring the above instructions.

(Note: The Square Stance is sometimes referred to as the Bow Stance. However, we will continue to refer to it as the Square Stance as this step is of a particular length, while the Bow Stance can be performed with longer or narrower distancing of the feet.)

EXERCISE 3: WEIGHT TRANSFER

A Commencing from a Left-foot Square Stance, while keeping your back straight and your body facing the same direction as your front foot, slowly transfer your weight onto your back foot and hold for a count of three.

B Slowly transfer weight onto your front foot. Make sure your knees are still bent and pointing in the same direction as your toes. Hold for a count of three.

C Repeat steps A and B six times, then repeat in a Right-foot Square Stance.

EXERCISE 4: WEIGHT TRANSFER WITH BALANCE

A Commencing from a Left-foot Square Stance, while keeping your back straight and your body facing the same direction as your front foot, draw in your back, or right, foot to side of your front foot. Make sure your knees are still bent and pointing in same direction as your toes. Keeping your right foot off the ground, hold for a count of three.

B Place your 'empty', or right, foot back in Left-foot Square Stance, placing your toes down first.

C Slowly transfer all your weight onto your back, or right, foot and draw in your front foot to the side of your back foot. Make sure your knees are still bent and pointing in same direction as your toes. Keeping your left foot off the ground, hold for a count of three.

D Place your 'empty', or left, foot back in the Left-foot Square stance, placing your heel down first. Slowly transfer your weight onto your front, or left, foot.

E Repeat steps A to D six times, then repeat in a Right-foot Square Stance.

EXERCISE 5: WEIGHT TRANSFER WITH WAIST TURN

A Commencing from a Left-foot Square Stance, slowly transfer all your weight back onto your rear, or right, foot (keep both feet on the ground). As your weight moves back, turn through your waist as far as comfortable to the right and hold for a count of three.

B Slowly transfer weight forward onto your left foot. As your weight moves forward, turn your waist back to face the front. Make sure your knees are still bent and pointing in same direction as your toes.

C Repeat steps A and B six times, then repeat in the Right-foot Square Stance (turning, through your waist, to the left).

EXERCISE 6: SQUARE STANCE WITH SENSITIVITY
(You will need a partner to perform this exercise.)

Face each other in a Square Stance, with your feet positioned so that the lead toes of each person are placed on an imaginary line drawn between both of you.

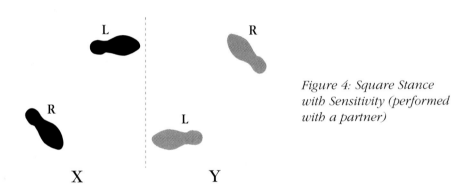

Figure 4: Square Stance with Sensitivity (performed with a partner)

A Commencing from a Left-foot Square Stance, each person places their fingertips lightly against the fingertips of the other. Shoulders, elbows and wrists are kept relaxed throughout.

B One person (let us call them X) now begins to transfer their weight forward. As they do so, the hands are kept in the same position, which means that X transmits the forward movement to the other person (let us call them Y) through the fingertips. In response, Y tries to maintain the same pressure at the fingertips by moving the weight onto the back leg.

C At the completion of X's forward movement, Y begins to transfer their weight forward. As they do so, the hands are kept in the same position, which means that Y transmits the forward movement to X through the fingertips. In response, X tries to maintain the same pressure at the fingertips by moving the weight onto the back leg.

D Repeat C to D six times, then change to a Right-foot Square Stance and repeat.

Bow Stance

As mentioned in the earlier note on page 26, a Square Stance is sometimes referred to as a Bow Stance, but the term Bow Stance is applied to any stance where the front foot points forwards and the rear foot is on a 45-degree angle. The stance can be longer, usually one half-step or one full-step, or narrower. The increase in length will depend on your level of ability and comfort and is, thus, a more advanced technique. Exercises 3–6 can be done in an extended Bow Stance.

Stepping on the Square

While there are a number of stepping techniques within the Tai Chi form, the Stepping on the Square technique can be regarded as the predominant one.

Square Step to the Right

A   Commencing from the Shoulder-width Stance, bend your knees as far as comfortable. Keep your back straight.

B   Transfer all your weight onto your left foot and lift your right foot in preparation for stepping out into the square.

C   Turning through your waist, step out on the square 90 degrees to the right, placing the foot down heel first. Transfer as much weight as comfortable onto your right foot and adjust your left toes 45 degrees to the right. Make sure your knees are still bent and pointing in same direction as your toes. Try to keep at the same height and not bob up and down.

Shoulder-width Stance

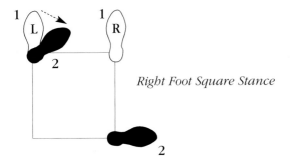

Right Foot Square Stance

Figure 5: Square Step to the Right

Square-Step to the Left

A Commencing from the Shoulder-width Stance, bend your knees as far as comfortable. Keep your back straight.

B Transfer all your weight onto your right foot and lift your left leg in preparation for stepping out into the square.

C Turning through your waist, step out on the square 90 degrees to the left, placing your foot down heel first. Transfer as much weight as comfortable onto your left foot and adjust your right foot 45 degrees to the left. Make sure your knees are still bent and pointing in same direction as your toes. Try to keep at the same height and not bob up and down.

Once you feel comfortable with performing the single steps, you can turn this exercise into a stepping flow pattern by square-stepping to the right, followed by weight transfer onto the right foot and then square-stepping immediately to the left, then right again, and so on. This practise will help you to prepare for the flowing on of the movements in the Tai Chi exercises given in Chapter 4.

Principles of Tai Chi stepping

The objective of Tai Chi stepping enable you to change the position of your feet while maintaining the five essential principles oulined in Chapter 2—relaxation, concentration, meditation, harmony and breathing. There are a number of points to remember in Tai Chi stepping, and they are as follows.

Rooting

Your 'root' foot, or supporting foot, must be firm while placing your 'empty' foot in position. There should be a sense of 'sinking' onto your supporting foot while your empty foot is being raised and placed. This should not be exaggerated and should be more 'mind intent'—in order to offset the risk of either bending the knee of the supporting leg more than is comfortable or of rising on the supporting leg, which often accompanies stepping.

Posture

Correct posture must be maintained while stepping—keep a straight back and hold your head up (but not tilted backwards, and your chin tucked in). If you do not retain this posture throughout a movement, your balance and inner strength will be lost.

Do not follow your stepping foot with your eyes. The *Tai Chi Ching Classics* say to 'walk like a cat'. A cat does not look where it is placing its paw, but it will not transfer its weight onto it before it is satisfied with its step. In other words, use your sense of touch: if you are not happy with the ground under your foot, adjust your foot and then, when you are satisfied, transfer your weight.

This is one reason for practising out in parks and areas where the ground is uneven, and where there may even be rocks and holes. Practising in sand, particularly at the edge of the sea where the waves are constantly washing the sand from under your feet, is beneficial because you have to constantly sense the changes and adjust your feet. As you progress, make a point of seeking out some more challenging surfaces, such as ones with slopes, to experience another side of your Tai Chi.

Relax the empty foot

Because your mind is focused on where to place your empty foot, there can be a tendency to hold the foot stiffly around the ankles and toes. This reduces the flow of blood and *chi* in your lower leg and foot. The injunction of the *Tai Chi Ching Classics* to 'walk like a cat' also tells us that this is wrong. When a cat's paw is supporting its weight, its toes are forward and there is a definite 'foot'. When the paw is lifted, the 'foot' becomes completely relaxed and almost seems to blend into the leg.

One technique to encourage relaxation in your feet is to 'walk with your knees'. This means that your focus is on lifting and lowering your knees. You mentally ignore your foot but, obviously, as you raise your knee, your foot will be lifted from the ground. Your heel comes off first, then the front of your foot, which should hang down slightly lower than the heel. The mechanics of the move then depend on where you are stepping. Try these exercises:

- To step forwards, incline your lower leg forwards about 45 degrees. Even though your forward foot is relaxed, the front of the foot is now higher than the heel and thus when you lower your knee, the heel will naturally come in contact with the ground first.
- To step backwards, incline your lower leg backwards about 45 degrees. This means that your toe is now significantly lower than your heel and will naturally come in contact with the ground first.
- To step sideways, incline your lower leg outwards about 45 degrees. Since the front part of your foot is lower than your heel, the inside edge of the front of your foot contacts the ground first, followed by the inside edge of your heel. The outside edge of your foot comes into contact with the ground last.

An example of a movement which involves stepping to the side is Cross Hands (see Chapter 4, page 82). In this move, first contact the ground with the inside edge of the stepping foot and roll the weight across the foot. Stepping in this manner not only accords with sound movement dynamics, but allows an additional range of movement within the foot.

The consequent massaging effect on the foot, the various flows of *chi* stimulated within the foot and the stimulation of acupressure points can also have additional health benefits.

Special notes

Double-weightedness

If one discounts the fact that the Tai Chi set commences from the basic-parallel stance (or the Shoulder-width Stance), the Cross Hands move (page 82) is the first move where you encounter the weight being held evenly on both feet. If you have read the *Tai Chi Ching Classics*, it may, on the surface, appear as though this posture is not in accordance with the injunction to, 'avoid double-weightedness'; that is, balancing your weight equally on both feet. A fuller reading of this injunction shows a deeper meaning to the principle: 'To avoid the fault of double-weighted-ness one must know *yin* and *yang*' (Treatise by Wang Tsung Yueh). That is, double weightedness is actually an extension of this ancient principle of differentiating *yin* and *yang*. In this move, the *yang* element is the upward blocking movement, while the *yin* element is the sinking and rooting of the feet. *Yin* and *yang* are thereby differentiated and there is no double-weightedness.

The 'silk-like' foot

It is important to remember that the principles applying to the use of the upper limbs also apply to the lower limbs. Thus, the movements of the legs and feet should be slow, even and without jerkiness, like pulling a silk thread from a silkworm's cocoon.

The three crystal bowls

Visualise your head, shoulder and pelvic areas as three crystal bowls filled with water. The objective in square stepping is to move so that you do not tilt any of these 'bowls' and thus spill the water contained within them. If your knee is raised so that your upper leg is higher than your hip, your pelvis will be tilted: you should only raise your knee as far as is necessary for your foot to clear the floor. The lesson here is to avoid overly dramatic movements—move only as much as necessary.

Bringing the empty foot into the side of the supporting foot

There is some discretion in this, and you can take the most direct route to the stepping position. However, bringing the foot in accords with the principle of keeping your options open as long as possible. This may not seem so important in a preset form, when you know which move will follow, but it is important in San Shou, or free-form Tai Chi, so that when the foot is brought in, the step may be in any of three directions or may be converted into a defensive stance or a kick.

Breathing

This section explains the breathing techniques used in Tai Chi. Breathing techniques vary with the objective of the art being performed, and the technique used in Tai Chi is an important part of the practice of the form.

The objectives of the Tai Chi breathing techniques are to:

- Supply all of the body's needs in terms of oxygen intake and carbon dioxide removal.
- Initiate the relaxation response.
- Maximise the absorption of *chi* from the air.
- Increase the blood supply to the internal organs by 'massaging' them through movement of the lung diaphragm.

Before looking further at Tai Chi breathing, we must first differentiate between Tai Chi breathing for martial arts purposes and Tai Chi breathing when the form is used as a health exercise.

Tai Chi breathing for martial arts or health purposes

When Tai Chi is used as a martial art, the focus is on short-term survival; that is, the nature of the combat will dictate the speed and nature of the movements, which in turn generate specific oxygen requirements.

The *Tai Chi Ching Classics* enjoin the practitioner to 'breathe naturally'; in this case, to allow your body's involuntary systems to control your breathing rate, so that the oxygen requirements for fuelling your muscles will be correctly met. The length and rate of your breathing will vary considerably, depending on the demands of the movement.

When Tai Chi is used as a health art, the focus is on long-term survival. The amount of oxygen that the body receives depends on the number of breaths per minute and the volume of air taken into the lungs with each breath. If you simply deepen your breathing you will naturally increase the supply of oxygen and the removal of carbon dioxide. Your body will respond by slowing your rate of respiration, so that your oxygen needs and supply are matched.

If you attempt to regulate both the frequency of breath and the volume of breath by conscious control, then you will probably cause a mismatch in oxygen supply and oxygen need. This will alter your body's basic biochemistry and may have deleterious effects. The result is known in the West as hyper- and hypo-ventilation. Symptoms include nausea and giddiness and, when carried to extremes, may cause loss of consciousness.

You should therefore allow your breathing rate to remain natural—that is, as dictated by your body's own internal control systems. The *Tai Chi Ching Classics* are correct in not drawing any distinction in the requirement to use natural breathing for Tai Chi, whether the art is used for combat or for health purposes.

The rate at which we breathe does, however, have a profound effect on our body's metabolism, particularly the heart rate and the stimulation of the sympathetic nervous system (which puts the body into its flight or fight mode when breathing is faster than normal). Therefore, slowing your breathing rate is a good objective, if done by indirect means. Thus, when using Tai Chi for health purposes, it is acceptable to use techniques that will increase the volume of air in each breath, as long as you allow your body to determine the overall oxygen supply by naturally decreasing the frequency of your breaths.

The difference, then, between Tai Chi breathing for martial arts purposes and Tai Chi breathing for health exercise is that, in the former case, the movements (which ensure short-term survival) are allowed to dictate the frequency of breath, whereas in the latter case we consciously seek to reduce the frequency of breath by deepening the volume of breath. This will generally require that the Tai Chi be performed at a slow pace.

There is one other difference—in the martial arts, the synchronisation of breath with movement can be very important in terms of the total effectiveness of the move. When performing Tai Chi for health purposes, this is less critical than keeping your breathing fluid and even. You may find, for instance, that when performing as part of a group, the speed of the movements may not suit your own breathing pattern. In this instance it is better not to synchronise breath and movement—just follow the injunction of the *Tai Chi Ching Classics* to breathe naturally.

Techniques used for Tai Chi breathing

In addition to the prime injunction to keep the rate of breathing natural and unforced, there are a number of other techniques that are associated with Tai Chi breathing. These include:

- Breathing in and out through your nose.
- Keeping your mouth closed, teeth slightly apart and your jaw relaxed.
- Holding your tongue with its tip placed behind the back of the upper teeth or, preferably, against the upper palate.
- Directing your breath mentally down to the *tan tien* (or abdomen). This aids using the lung diaphragm, so that it presses down on the organs in the abdominal cavity on each in-breath (thereby massaging them).
- Keeping your breath unforced. Your approach to breathing should be natural and relaxed.
- Smoothing the breath to eliminate any jerkiness in your movements as your in-breath changes to out-breath, and vice versa.
- Quietening your breath so that you can barely hear it.
- Keeping your posture correct is critical for good breathing. Keep your head erect, as though lifted through the *bai hui* point (the highest point of your head; refer to the diagram showing acupoints, Chapter 1, page 14), your shoulders relaxed and your pelvis tucked forward.

Breathing rhythm

Everyone has their own breathing rhythm. When practising with a group, match the slowest rhythm that is comfortably attainable by all, as this is more likely to benefit those who are newer to the art. Forcing people to breathe at a slower rate than what they are comfortable with causes stress and tension. Children, in particular, have a higher rate of respiration than adults, and may find Tai Chi uncomfortable to perform at an adult pace. This is one reason why it is good to perform some quietening exercises, which allow the respiration rate to drop, before starting Tai Chi.

Candle-breathing exercise

Standing quietly, close your eyes and visualise a lighted candle, the flame of which is about five centimetres (two inches) from the tip of your nose. As you breathe in and out through your nose, do so with such smoothness and gentleness that if the candle were real its flame would not even flicker. Focus especially on the changes from inhalation to exhalation, and vice versa, as this will make for a gentle, rather than abrupt, change between breathing in and out.

Only when you have understood and practised the above techniques, should you commence performing the exercises in the following chapter.

CHAPTER 4

Movements
LEVELS 1 AND 2

Learning how to perform Tai Chi

Learning the movements is only the first step to performing Tai Chi—
what is often called the 'outer' form. Also applying to every move are the
Tai Chi principles, as described in the previous chapters of this book.
Once you have established the outer form of a movement, refer to the
general principles and techniques of the art—applying these will lead
you to the 'inner' form.

To assist you with the development of both 'outer' and 'inner' forms, I
have also included with each movement description a deeper look at the
move, including such aspects as:

- the imagery associated with the move
- the flow of *chi* throughout the move
- common problems associated with performing the move, along with
  ways of identifying and resolving them.

Movement directions

The movements include directions—down, up, front, back, left and right—indicating that the part of the body being described faces or moves directly in that direction.

Where I have used less definite terms—upwards, downwards, forwards and backwards—this indicates that the part of the body being described faces or moves in that general, rather than absolute, direction.

During your Tai Chi, parts of your body will often be held on a slant or angle. Where I indicate two directions—such as 'Palm faces forwards and downwards'—this indicates that your palm is at an angle between directly downwards and directly forwards. This is better than saying 'Palm inclines upwards at an angle of 45 degrees' as this indicates a level of precision that is not required. Angles are used in specifying footwork only, because this is the most simple, effective description. Accuracy within 10 degrees or so is fine!

Do not be rigid with your Tai Chi. When standing, never hold your knees, nor your elbows or wrists, stiffly. Tai Chi positions are never forcedly straight.

In the following exercises I will sometimes instruct you to put your knees in the 'off-lock' position. You can find the 'off-lock' position by first straightening your knees, then lowering your body downwards by pushing your knees slightly forward. (In other words, just relax your knees to allow your body to relax downwards.)

I also use the term 'open' to indicate that the arms should be held as if there is a tiny ball nestled in your armpit, or resting on the inside of your elbow joint.

Following the pattern of the movements

The movements included in this chapter are not to be thought of as being separate exercises. One key aspect of Tai Chi is its flow, and the movements in Levels 1 and 2 follow directly on from each other. Tai Chi is a continuous flow of form changing from one posture to another. If this is your first introduction to Tai Chi, I suggest you do, however, practise each movement several times before moving on to the next one.

Each movement description is divided into two parts:

- the first part of the movement description indicates the physical aspects of the move;
- the second, what you need to consider when performing the move.

Although you will initially need to concentrate on the physical form of the moves, in the effort of trying to master each move don't forget that the most important thing in your Tai Chi practice is to feel comfortable. You will not be able to relax if you put your body into positions that strain it. And stressing over whether or not you have got the movement exactly right isn't the point either!

Most importantly, don't forget to breathe naturally. Relax into your Tai Chi and enjoy the freedom of the movements. Again, I cannot emphasise enough that you should employ the main principles of Tai Chi in your practice—this will get you most of the way to the correct performance of Tai Chi. Eventually your body will become familiar with the movements —give yourself time, and practise!

When starting your Tai Chi practice:

- Look at the photographs of the movement to gain a visual understanding of what you are about to do.
- Read the instructions for the move you are about to perform. Remember the physical aspects are given first, followed by considerations that will improve your performance once you can follow the movement.
- I have included each movement's imagery directly under its heading, as it will help you to gain a better impression of the flow of the movement. If you prefer to use imagery of your own, please do so.
- If this is your first experience of Tai Chi, practise each move several times before you move on to the next one.
- Finally, put all the moves together in one continuous flow.
- In your initial practice, don't be too concerned about your breathing.

Breathe naturally. As you progress with your ability to perform the movements, try following the breathing patterns I have given for each movement.

● Under the heading *Chi coordination* at each move, directions are given to help you coordinate your mental focus on the *chi* with a particular aspect of a move; to visualise yourself drawing in or extending *chi* from the prescribed area is all that is required. Refer to Chapter 1, page 14, for further details concerning focusing on the *chi* in your body.

Essential points to remember when performing Tai Chi

● Employ the five essential principles: relaxation, concentration, meditation, harmony and breathing. (Refer to Chapter 2 for further details on these principles.)

● Never strain to perform a movement—only go as far as you comfortably can.

● Play Tai Chi. Tai Chi is not supposed to be performed with grim determination. One should relax, enjoy and have fun with one's Tai Chi.

● Smile through your eyes. A 'mental' smile not only benefits the body, but puts you in the right frame of mind to do Tai Chi.

● Relax! Relax! Relax! Do not hold your breath. Just go with the flow of the movement.

It cannot be emphasised enough that the physical positioning of the body represents only the outer form. It is the application of the Tai Chi principles to mind and body that constitutes the important inner form. Do not become excessively preoccupied with a movement's position.

Preparation Movement

Also known as Figure Eight

You can apply this formal opening movement to any exercise set where there is a requirement to step out to a Shoulder-width Stance, or a wider one.

• As well as the purely mechanical function of establishing the correct starting position, this opening movement also encourages the correct mental state for performing Tai Chi (comfortably relaxed with a quiet awareness of your body and surroundings) and the appropriate breathing (relaxed and unforced natural breathing gradually allowing your breath to go deeper into your belly).

• The movement is designed to centre you, sink your *chi* (by relaxing your body on the out breath and gradually sinking and focusing your breath into your *tan tien*—your abdomen, about three fingerwidths below your navel) and raise your *shen* (or 'lift your spirit' to project your feeling or thought to the top

of your head; this imagery also helps lengthen your spine).

The alternative name for this position— Figure Eight—is derived from its starting position: with heels together and toes apart the feet form the same shape as the Chinese symbol for the number eight. (To Chinese people, the number eight carries significant connotations of good fortune and health.)

Leg work

• Place your feet together at the heels, with your toes separated and pointing 45 degrees away from the centreline of your body. Your knees should be off-lock, with your weight balanced equally on both feet.

• Your arms should be loose at the side of your body, but not touching it, with your palms facing inwards. Your fingers should be gently extended but not straight. Your arms should remain completely relaxed throughout the movement.

• Keeping your back straight gently sink your body by bending your knees until they are positioned above your toes. (This will bring your body to the height at which the remainder of the set will be performed.)

• Transfer your weight to your right foot, lift your left heel off the ground and turn your body to the right.

• Raise your left knee sufficiently for your left foot to clear the ground in a relaxed state and step out shoulder-width distance to the left.

• Lower your left knee so that the right side of your left foot is placed in contact with the ground first. Your left heel should now be shoulder-distance from your right heel, your toes pointing directly forwards.

• Transfer your weight to your left foot, turn your body to the left, raising the ball of your right foot and turning it to point directly forwards, so that both feet are parallel.

• Transfer your weight back so that it is equally placed on both feet and straighten your legs to the off-lock position.

Key points

• Stand upright naturally.

• Keep your head slightly raised and your chin relaxed inwards.

• Relax your body and breathe naturally.

• Keep your upper body erect (that is, do not lean) while it is turning and your centre of gravity is shifting.

Breathing and Coordination

• Keep your lips closed, with your teeth separated, and breathe through your nose.

• Before moving, take several calming breaths, with your mind focused on the *tan tien* (abdomen).

• When centred, breathe in and, on the first exhalation, sink and transfer your weight.

• On the second inhalation step out to shoulder-width position and transfer your weight to the left.

• On the second exhalation centre your weight.

• On the third inhalation rise to the knee off-lock position.

• On the third exhalation relax any tension.

• On the fourth inhalation, staying relaxed, feel yourself fill with *chi*.

Chinese character for eight

Further information

The opening movement prepares the body physically, mentally, emotionally and energetically for the Tai Chi set. All you really need to remember is what I call the 'three keys of Tai Chi': relaxation, posture and comfort.

• *The first part of the preparation is relaxation. Don't just relax the muscles, relax also at a mental, emotional and energetic level. To do this, feel the body become heavier, the tensions flow downwards, the breath slow and deepen, let go any mental worries and emotional tensions. Visualise the body becoming quiet and still.*

• *Now, within the relaxation, assume not only a physical, but also a mental, emotional and energetic posture. Become aware of your surroundings, visualise the energy of your body rising, and focus your mind.*

• *Finally, check for comfort at each level. Adjust your posture and degree of relaxation until you are comfortable. Now you are ready for Tai Chi.*

Commencement Movement

Also known as Floating Hands

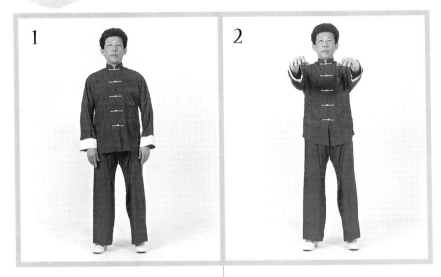

Imagery

Imagine your hands resting on a large helium-filled balloon that slowly rises, lifting your hands to shoulder-height. There, your hands slide up, over and off the balloon and sink slowly, in front and to the side of your hips.

Leg work

- To commence, your feet should be parallel and shoulder-width apart, your weight equally balanced on both feet and centred between the toes and heel of each foot. Check your knees are in the off-lock position and face the same direction as your toes (1).
- Lower your body by bending your knees to a comfortable degree.

Arm work

- Commence with both your arms hanging loosely by the sides of your body. Check

your palms face inwards, your fingers are gently extended but not stretched, your armpits are open and your shoulders are relaxed (1).

- Raise your arms, with your palms inclined towards each other, to shoulder-height (2).
- Drop your elbows, raise your palms to eye-level and rotate them inwards so that they face downwards.
- Drop your wrists and lower your arms so that your hands come to rest at about hip-height, slightly in front of your body. Check your palms face downwards, your fingers point forwards, gently extended but not stretched, your armpits are open and your shoulders relaxed (3).

Coordination

- Bring your hands up to shoulder-height then, as you sink, bring your hands down.

Key points

• Keep your head upright and your gaze level.
• Hold your shoulders and your elbows downwards.
• Relax your spine and back.

Further information

Breathing

• *Breathe in as you raise your hands.*
• *Breathe out as you lower your hands.*

Chi coordination

Visualise the chi at the Hegu points (refer to Chapter 1, Figure X, page 14) as you raise your hands, and at the lao gong points in your palms as you press your hands down.

There should always be a feeling of extension of chi through the yong quan points of the feet

when they are in contact with the ground. (From now on, attention will only be directed to this during stepping movements, when the sense of sinking chi through the yong quan point of the supporting foot is most important to establish stability and rooting to the ground.)

Common problems with the move

• *Tense shoulders. Don't lift your elbows above shoulder-height, as this will result in tension in your shoulders. You should feel as though your hands, on their upward movement, are pushing away from your spine. In this way you will retain the power of the movement.*
• *Arms in too close to your chest. This cuts the flow of blood and chi at the elbow. Allow your elbows to move out and down as you draw in. Finish the move with your hands at hip height, about 15 centimetres (six inches) in front of your body—do not bring them in to your sides.*
• *Palms facing away from each other on the upward movement (rather than downwards). Doing this turns your elbow joints outwards, effectively locking them. This means that your elbows and wrists will both rise to shoulder-height on the upward movement of the hands, and this will raise your shoulders. If your hands are inclined towards each other, it is easy to keep your elbows relaxed, open and lower than your wrists, thus keeping your arms more relaxed.*

Holding the Ball to the Right

Also known as Embracing the Moon.

Imagery

Imagine holding a large beach ball—your right hand on top of the ball, your left hand underneath. Remember that such a ball has three dimensions, not two, and that it is therefore necessary to hold the ball out from your chest. Do not exaggerate this so much that you put tension into your shoulders or lean forwards. (Some practitioners imagine the ball as the silvery, glowing moon, hence the alternative title.)

Leg work

- Transfer your weight to your left foot. Raise the ball of your right foot, leaving your right heel on the ground (1).
- Turn your right foot by pivoting on your right heel so that the toes on your right foot point out to the right, 90 degrees from the starting position. Check your left knee still

faces in the same direction as the toes on your left foot (1).
- Transfer your weight to your right foot and draw your left foot in alongside, counterbalancing on the ball of the foot but leaving the foot empty (2).

Body work

- Turn your body 90 degrees to the right.

Arm work

- Arc your right hand to eye level, opposite the centreline of your body. Your palm faces down, your fingers point to the left. Check your elbow is down, your shoulders relaxed, your armpit is open and your arm in a gentle curve (2).

At the same time:
- Rotate your left palm so that it faces up and bring your left hand under the right one,

at *tan tien* (abdomen) height. Check your fingers point to the right, your armpit is open and your arm is in a gentle curve.

Coordination

- Start the move by transferring your weight to the left and lifting the toes of your right foot.
- As you turn your body, open your right foot outwards and bring your arms into position.
- Finally, lower the toes of your right foot and transfer your weight to your right leg. At the same time relax your shoulders and arms.

Key Points

- Relax your shoulders and elbows downwards and keep your arms in a curve.
- Keep your body in balance while shifting your centre of gravity.
- Transfer your weight smoothly.
- Keep your tailbone tucked in and your head up.
- Look directly ahead of your body throughout the movement.
- At the end of the movement make sure your arms are in gentle curves, and your armpits and elbow joint open.

Further information

Breathing

- *Breathe in as you bring your hands into position.*
- *Breathe out as you sink your weight into your right foot and release tension from your arms.*

Chi coordination

Visualise a connection between the lao gong *points of each hand, as though* chi *flows between them.*

Common problems with the move

- *Holding the ball too far away or too close to the body.*
- *Making the ball too large or too small.*
- *Stiff shoulders. Ensure your shoulders are relaxed, your spine upright and that* chi *and blood are able to flow freely.*
- *An experiment: To check the correct positioning of your right hand take hold of your right wrist with your left hand. If you can easily pull your right hand towards your body then you need to increase the degree of curvature in your right arm. Experiment until you find a point where strength flows into the curved arm. This means that* chi *and blood can also flow easily.*

Grasping the Bird's Tail

Imagery

Imagine a bird, the size of a parrot or pigeon, standing on your left wrist, and your right hand drawing downwards from the bird's head to its tail in a stroking motion. At the end of the movement, imagine watching the bird fly from your wrist: this is important, otherwise the eyes will tend to follow the movement of the right hand, resulting in the head dropping and a loss of posture.

Leg work

• Square-step to the left (see page 30) and transfer 70 per cent of your weight to your left foot. Adjust your right foot by either turning your toes inwards or pushing your heel outwards so that you face the front (3).

Body work

• Turn your body 90 degrees to the left.

Arm work

• Arc your left hand up so that it finishes at chest-height. Check that your palm faces your chest, your arm is in a gentle curve, your fingers point to the right, your armpit is open and your shoulder relaxed (3). At the same time:
• Draw your right hand down so that it finishes at hip-height on the right side of your body. Check your palm faces down, your fingers point to the front, your armpit is open and your shoulder relaxed (3). (Your hands therefore pass each other at close range as you slowly stroke the bird from head to tail.)

Coordination

• The movement starts with the stepping out of the left foot (1).
• As you transfer your weight to your left

foot and turn, your left arm rises and your right arm draws down (2 and 3).
• Finally, adjust your right foot. At the same time, relax your shoulders and arms.

Key Points
• Keep both your arms relaxed and curved.
• Your stepping should be relaxed.
• The movement of your upper and lower limbs should be completed simultaneously.
• At the end of this movement, check your knees are bent and are facing in the same direction as your toes, and make sure your arms are in gentle curves, with the inside of your elbow joint open.

Further information

Breathing
• Breathe in as you step.

• Breathe out as you transfer your weight and bring your hands into position.

Chi coordination
Visualise the chi being expressed mainly through the lao gong point of your right palm as it sweeps down to stroke the bird's tail. You should visualise the chi along the outer edge of your left forearm and along the back of your hand. Do not forget to sense the chi moving down through the yong quan point of the supporting foot.

Common problems with the move
• Holding the left hand too close to the body. An Experiment: To check that your left hand is in the correct position, refer to the experiment for Holding the Ball to the Right, page 46.

Holding the Ball to the Left

At the same time:
- Rotate your right hand so that the palm faces up. Draw it upwards to *tan tien* (abdomen) height, bringing it directly below your left palm, fingertips pointing to the left. Check that your armpit is open and your shoulder relaxed.

Coordination
- Start the movement by turning your waist to the left. At the same time, rotate your hands and bring your arms into position.
- As you transfer your weight to your left foot, release any tension from your arms and shoulders.

Key Points
Refer to Holding the Ball to the Right, page 47.

Further information

Breathing
- *Breathe in as you turn and bring your arms into position.*
- *Breathe out as you transfer your weight and sink slightly.*

Chi coordination
Refer to Holding the Ball to the Right, page 47.

Common problems with the move
Refer to Holding the Ball to the Right, page 47.

Imagery
The imagery for this move is the same as for Holding the Ball to the Right, page 46, but with your left hand on top.

Leg work
- Transfer all of your weight to your left foot and draw in your right foot to the side of your left foot. Your right foot should remain empty.

Body work
- Turn your body 45 degrees to the left.

Arm work
- Rotate your left hand so that your palm faces downwards and your fingers point to the right. Check that your arm is in a gentle curve, that your armpit is open and your shoulder is relaxed (1).

Ward Off

Imagery

Imagine a swallow landing on a moving branch.

Leg Work

• Square-step to the right (see page 29) and transfer 70 per cent of your weight to your right foot.
• Adjust your left foot by either turning your toes inwards or pushing your heel outwards.

Body work

• Turn your body 135 degrees to the right, so that you face in the same direction as your right foot.

Arm work

• Arc your right hand upwards until it is at heart-height, your palm facing your body, your fingers pointing to the left. Check your arm is in a gentle curve, your shoulder is relaxed, your elbow points downwards, and your armpit and elbow joint are open.
At the same time:
• Drop your left elbow and wrist so your left palm faces forwards from your body, your fingers pointing upwards at an angle, and bring the fingertips of your left hand up behind your right wrist, making a T-shape.

Coordination

• Step out with your right foot as you turn your body and start moving your arms.
• Transfer your weight and complete the arm movements.

Key points

• Relax your shoulders and hold your elbows down.
• Keep your arms in a curve.
• Keep your upper body erect.
• At the end of this movement, check your knees are bent and facing in the same direction as your toes.

Further information

Breathing

• Breathe in as you place your foot and bring your arms into position.
• Breathe out as you transfer your weight and finish the move.

Chi coordination

Visualise the chi in the lao gong point of your left palm and the leading outer edge of your right forearm and back of your right hand.

Pull Back and Press Forward

Imagery

For the pull back, imagine pulling on a rope or drawing in a net. For the press, imagine yourself pressing forwards against a heavy object.

Leg work

- Transfer 70 per cent of your weight to your left foot (2). Pull back.
- Transfer 70 per cent of your weight to your right foot (4). Press forward.

Body work

- Turn your body 45 degrees to the left (2).
- Turn your body 45 degrees to the right (4).

Arm work

- Rotate your left hand anticlockwise so that your palm faces upwards, and your fingers point forwards (1).

At the same time:

- Turn your right hand so that your right palm faces slightly downwards and outwards, fingers pointing forwards (1).
- Draw both your arms downwards, keeping them fairly extended. Your left hand movement finishes slightly to the left of your left hip, with the palm facing upwards and fingers pointing outwards; your right hand finishes to the front of your left hip, with the palm facing downwards and fingers pointing outwards.
- Continue to draw your left hand leftwards, arcing it up to shoulder-height, palm facing outwards (3).

At the same time:

- Raise your right hand to heart-height and rotate it so that your palm faces your body, fingers pointing to the left (3).
- Drop your left elbow and draw your left hand in towards your right hand, placing the

base of your left hand against your right wrist. The fingers of your left hand should point upwards (3).

• Extend your arms forwards as far as comfortable. Do not straighten either arm, keep your shoulders and elbows relaxed (4). (Much of the arm work is controlled by the turning of your body.)

Coordination

• As you commence the weight transfer, prepare your hands.

• As you complete the weight transfer, draw your hands down.

• Let your left hand float up to shoulder-height, then turn your body to the right and bring your hands together in front of your chest.

• Transfer your weight and extend your arms.

Key points

• Relax your lower back and hips.

• Your arm movements should follow your turning body.

• Keep your upper body erect and your shoulders relaxed.

Further information

Breathing

• Breathe in as you transfer your weight back.

• Breathe out as you transfer weight forwards.

Chi coordination

For the Pull Back imagine a connection between your left fingertips and the heel of your right hand. Sense chi in your hands, and at the lao gong points. For the Press, visualise chi in the left hand's lao gong point and the leading edge of your right forearm and back of your right hand.

Push to Close the Door

Imagery
Imagine pushing to close a heavy door (such as you might see in an old temple or church).

Leg work
• Transfer 70 per cent of your weight to your back foot (2).
• Transfer 70 per cent of your weight to your front foot (3).

Body work
• There is a very slight leftwards movement of your body as you draw back, and a rightwards movement of your body as you move forwards, so that at the end your body faces forwards.

Arm work
• Turn your right palm to face downwards and slide your left palm over the back of your right hand, separating your hands to shoulder-width. Check your palms face down and fingers point forwards (1).
• Drop your wrists as you draw your elbows back, bringing your hands down to about heart-height. Check your arms are curved, your palms face forwards and your fingers point upwards (2).
• Gently push your hands forwards and upwards to about chest-height. Check your elbows are dropped, allowing your palms to face forwards without bending your wrists too much. Your hands remain shoulder-width apart (3).

Coordination
• As you commence the weight transfer, complete the hand preparation. As you complete the weight transfer, draw your hands downwards.

3

• As you transfer your weight back to your right foot, push your palms forwards to chest-height.

Key points
• Push your body forwards to push your hands forwards.
• Body and hand work should be completed simultaneously.
• Your upper body must remain upright throughout the entire movement.
• At the end of this movement, check your knees are bent and facing in the same direction as your toes, your arms are in gentle curves, with your armpits and the inside of your elbow joints open.

Further information

Breathing
• Breathe in as you move back onto your left foot.
• Breathe out as you move forwards onto your right foot.

Chi coordination
Visualise the chi expressing through the lao gong points in both palms as you push your hands forwards and upwards.

Common problems with the move
• Leaning forwards into the push. Keep your body vertical.
• Bending your wrists too much. Keep your palms facing forwards by dropping your elbows and sloping your forearms.
• Drawing the hands too close to the body when preparing the push. Allow your elbows to come out to your sides rather than in towards your chest.
• Twisting through back knee when pushing forward. Always keep the back knee pointing in the same direction as the back toe. You will find that you are much stronger when the back knee is properly aligned and the back foot is firm on the floor.

Single Whip A (to the left)

Imagery

For the arm work in this movement, imagine the branches of a willow blowing in the breeze.

Leg work

• Transfer all of your weight to your left foot, and then lift the ball of your right foot (1).

• Turn your right foot 90 degrees to the left by pivoting on your heel and then place the right foot on the ground. Your right foot should have little or no weight on it (2). (This is one of the few times that the pelvic area is closed rather than open.)

Body work

• Turn your body 135 degrees to the left so that you face about 45 degrees left of centre —that is, between front and left.

Arm work

• Relax your wrists and drop your elbows. Check your armpits are open, your elbow and shoulder joints relaxed.

• Turn your left elbow out slightly so that your left palm is angled outwards. Make sure that whilst your palm is higher than your shoulder, your elbow is lower.

At the same time:

• Draw your right hand downwards to heart-height, rotating your wrist so that your palm is angled outwards.

Coordination

• Let your hands come into position as you draw your weight back into your left foot.

• Turn your body to the left and point the toes of your right foot to the front. Your arms will be swept leftwards from the turning motion of your body.

Key Points
- Keep your posture naturally expanded and upright.
- Complete the push to the left and the formation of the footwork simultaneously.

Further information

Breathing
- *Breathe in as you transfer your weight back and position your arms.*
- *Breathe out as you turn your body to the left.*

Chi coordination
Visualise the chi being expressed through the lao gong points of your hands and the yong quan point of the supporting foot.

Common problems with the move
- *Failing to keep the elbows below the shoulders and wrists, resulting in tension in the shoulders.*
- *Swaying the body instead of keeping it fully vertical.*
- *Thinking the movement is in the arms rather than the waist, which will result in bringing the arms too close to the body and cutting the flow of blood and chi. Experiment by keeping your arms frozen and moving your body. You will see 90 per cent of the arm movement is generated by the body movement.*

Special note regarding Tai Chi Ching Classics
The Tai Chi Ching Classics is a vast source of learning for all Tai Chi students and practitioners. Its invaluable advice can be applied to your Tai Chi, as shown in the following example.

- *One of the most important sayings from the Tai Chi Ching Classics is:*

  Movement is rooted in the feet, powered through the legs, directed by the waist and expressed in the hands.

If you keep this advice in mind when you are performing the move, you will more readily overcome many of the common problems associated with this movement.

Single Whip B (to the right)

Imagery
The imagery for this movement is the same as for Single Whip A, page 56.

Leg work
• Transfer your weight back to your right foot. Lift your left knee, thus raising your left heel, but leave the ball of your left foot on the ground (1).

Body work
• Turn your body 90 degrees to the right so that you face 45 degrees to the right of centre, that is midway between the front and right (2).

Arm work
• Draw your left hand downwards to heart-height, rotating your wrist so that your palm is angled outwards.

At the same time:
• Draw your right hand upwards to face-height, turning your elbow out slightly and rotating your right wrist so that your palm is angled outwards. Check your elbow is below shoulder level.

Coordination
• Transfer the position of your hands as you transfer your weight to your right foot.
• Turn your body to the right. (Your arms will be swept rightwards by this turning motion.)

Key points
• Keep your posture naturally expanded (that is, don't allow your posture to collapse inwards) and upright.
• Complete the push to the right and the formation of the footwork simultaneously.

Further information

Breathing
- Breathe in as you transfer your weight back and position your arms.
- Breathe out as you turn your body to the right.

Chi coordination
Visualise the chi being expressed through the lao gong points of your hands and the yong quan point of the supporting foot.

Common problems with the move
As for Single Whip A.

Special note
In the transition between this move and the next, the right hand forms into a hook. This often causes problems. So it is worthwhile to practise forming the hook separately before moving on to the next movement.

Form the hook by bringing the tips of your fingers and thumb together, as though caging a small bird inside your hand. (Fingers and thumb should be curved.) The wrist is relaxed and the tip of the hook points downwards to the ground.

One common problem at this stage of the Tai Chi set is a tendency to speed up too much, and the student needs to focus on maintaining a slow, uniform pace that is consistent throughout the set. A simple experiment can be performed that shows you just how significant the effect of the speed at which you perform Tai Chi is.

First, perform the Tai Chi you have learned at double your normal speed and take a few moments to see how you feel at the end. Now assume the shoulder stance position and take eight slow, deep, calming breaths and at the end of this commence your Tai Chi at half your normal speed. This will take considerable effort and concentration, but persevere and then compare how you feel with how you felt at the end of the double speed Tai Chi. You will find that you worked much harder in the half speed Tai Chi, and you will also feel much quieter and stiller than you did with the double speed Tai Chi.

This effect has been gained after only a few movements of Tai Chi, so you will appreciate how significant the difference in performing the entire Tai Chi set at different speeds can be. The faster you move, the faster you breathe and the lower your level of relaxation. The leg muscles particularly work much less as they now only have to support the full weight of the body for the short time the other leg is raised, so the toning of these muscles and the consequent enhancement of the venous blood system is much reduced.

Maintaining a slow speed requires constant vigilance. Visualising the body as moving through water not only tends to keep the speed of Tai Chi slow, but because we are visualising a motion as requiring more energy than the actual movement takes, the flow of Tai Chi is stimulated.

Single Whip C, Press

This movement is also sometimes called Embracing the Moon.

Imagery
Focus on a sense of gathering and expansion.

Leg work
• Pivot on the ball of your left foot. Then Square Step to the Left (refer page 30) and transfer 70 per cent of your weight to your left foot.

Body work
• Turn your body 135 degrees to the left in two stages: 90 degrees as the hook circles your left hand, then another 45 degrees when stepping out to press.

Arm work
• Rotate your left wrist so that your palm faces your face (as though you are looking in a mirror). Relax your left elbow but keep your left arm extended in a gentle curve (1).

At the same time:
• Form a hook with your right hand and arc it around and inwards so that it passes first behind and then in front of your left hand in 'mirror'.
• Start to draw the hook out to the right side of your body, at shoulder-height (2).
• Turn your left palm to face forwards and then extend your left arm in front of body at heart-height (3).
At the same time:
• Complete the extension through your right arm.

Coordination
• Turn your body to the left and bring the hook around in front of the mirror as your left leg pivots to the left.
• Step out to the left and turn your left palm outwards.

3

• Transfer your weight to the left as you press forwards with your left hand and complete the extension through your right arm.

Key points
• Keep your posture naturally expanded and upright.
• Complete the press and transfer of weight simultaneously.

Further information

Breathing
• Breathe in as you turn, pivot and circle the hook.
• Breathe out as you step and transfer your weight.

Chi coordination
Visualise the chi being expressed from the lao gong point of your left hand and in the hook of your right hand.

Common problems with the move
As for Single Whip A and B, but including:
• Bending the left wrist too much when pressing and thus cutting flow of blood and chi. Rather, keep your elbow down.
• Holding tension in your right wrist, resulting in the hook not pointing to the ground.
• Holding the left 'mirror' hand too close to your face and cutting the supply of blood and chi at your elbow.
• Holding the 'mirror' hand too low and bending your head to look towards it.
• Having too much tension in the hook by keeping your fingers straight rather than curved.

Play the Lute

Also known as Strumming the Lute

Imagery

The actual Chinese lute is supported against the body, with the right hand extended directly in front holding the neck of the instrument. The strings are strummed about halfway along the instrument, about opposite the elbow joint of the supporting arm. Imagine you are holding such an instrument.

Leg work

• Transfer your weight to your right foot. Complete this part of the move by lifting the ball of your left foot (1).

• Turn your left foot inwards 45 degrees and lower it to the ground, then transfer all of your weight to your left foot. To complete, raise your right heel slightly and allow your foot to straighten (2).

• Raise your right knee, thus lifting your right foot, and place your foot comfortably in front of you—your heel resting on the floor, your toes raised. Your left knee should be bent, with your lower right leg making an angle of about 45 degrees to the ground. There should be no weight on your right foot (3).

Body work

• Turn your body 90 degrees to the right
• Turn your body 45 degrees to the left
• Turn your body 45 degrees to the right.

Arm work

• Relax your left wrist and allow your palm to face downwards. Roll your left elbow and arc your arm downwards and forwards (1).
• Arc your left hand downwards until it passes your left hip, then arc it forwards until it is at heart-height, palm angled downwards and rightwards, fingers pointing forwards (2).

left foot, relax your right hand and begin the downwards arc.
• Turn your body to the left as you bring your right hand up in front of your body and raise your right leg.
• Turn your body to the right and place your hands and right leg simultaneously to form the Play the Lute posture.

Key points
• Keep the centre of gravity moving smoothly and at the same level.
• Your whole weight should be on your left leg in the final posture.

Further information

Breathing
• *Breathe in as you arc your left hand downwards.*
• *Breathe out as you bring your left hand up and arc your right hand down to hip height.*
• *Breathe in as you raise your right hand and right leg.*
• *Breathe out as you lower your right leg and position your hands.*

Chi coordination
Visualise chi being expressed from the lao gong points of your left and right hands as they arc downwards. In the Play the Lute posture, focus on the chi in the leading edges of your hands, and reinforce this by looking over your fingertips.

Common problems with the move
• *Holding the hands too close to your body in the Playing the Lute posture.*

• As your left hand completes its motion, release the hook in your right hand and arc it down following the pattern of the left hand. Bring your right hand up to chest-height, your palm facing left, your fingers angled upwards (2).
• As your right hand rises in front of your body your left hand sinks, bringing your left palm to face the inside of the right elbow. The fingers of your left hand are at about heart-height (3).

Coordination
• As you transfer your weight to your right foot, relax your left hand and begin the downwards arc.
• Turn your body to the right as you bring your left foot around and arc your left hand upwards in front of your body.
• As you transfer your weight back to your

Shoulder Stroke

Also known as the Shoulder Press

Imagery

The circling of the arms is like steering a big ship: imagine holding the wheel and turning it to the right. At the end of the move, imagine that the right side of your body is firm.

Leg work

• Lift your right knee slightly and let the ball of your right foot come in contact with the ground, raising the right heel. (This draws in your lower right leg, which should now be perpendicular to the ground).

• Transfer half of your weight to your right foot, at the same time raise the heel of your left foot. All your body weight should be equally supported by the balls of both feet.

• Pivot leftwards 90 degrees on the balls of your feet. (You will find that the toes of your right foot are more or less in line with your left heel and that your feet are substantially less than shoulder-width apart.)

• Lower your left heel to the ground and transfer all your weight to your left foot. Your right foot is empty, the heel raised (1).

• Lift your right knee and step outwards directly to your right, placing your right foot at a 45-degree angle. Check your heels are shoulder-width apart and in line (2).

• Transfer 70 per cent of your weight to your right foot. Check your knees are bent and facing in the same direction as your toes and your left foot is flat on the ground (3).

Body work

• During the pivot, your body turns 90 degrees to the left.

Arm work

• Push your right hand upwards and outwards in a large circle, continuing until your

3

• As you lower your left heel, complete the motion of your hands (2).
• Step to the side, transferring your weight to your right foot.
• Transfer your weight, turning your head to look over your right shoulder (3).

Key points
• Keep your upper body erect.
• Do the Shoulder Stroke with the stepping.

Further information

Breathing
• *Breathe in as you push your hands upwards and outwards.*
• *Breathe out as you step and transfer your weight.*

Chi coordination
Focus on the chi in the outside edge of your hands. Feel it throughout your hands as they circle into position for the shoulder press. As you sink your weight onto your left foot, visualise chi rooting down from the yong quan point on your left foot. As you perform the shoulder press, visualise the chi on the outer edge of your right shoulder, right hip and outside edge of your right upper leg. Focus your eyes strongly—this helps to direct the chi.

arm comes back across the front of your body at *tan tien* (abdomen) height. Your right palm faces up, and your fingers point left. At the same time:
• Move your left hand downwards and outwards in a large circle until your arm comes back across the front of your body at chest-height; the left palm tilted upwards to face right, fingers pointing upwards. The left hand positioning is done by partially dropping your left elbow and tilting your wrist. Your left thumb should be in line with your right armpit, your right hand under the left elbow (3).

Coordination
• As you draw your right foot in to pivot, start your right hand moving upwards and your left hand moving downwards.
• As you pivot, turning your body leftwards, bring your arms out to shoulder-height.

Common problems with the move
• *Avoid leading with the shoulders or hips, which throws the spine out of alignment and distorts the posture.*
• *In the circling movement of the hands, be sure to keep your armpits and elbows open.*

White Crane Spreads its Wings

Imagery

For this movement, visualise a crane spreading out its wings to dry its feathers under the warm sun. The movement should be delicate, yet firm and elegant, with the posture upright, yet relaxed.

Leg work

• Transfer all of your body weight into your right foot.
• Lift your left knee and bring your left foot forwards, allowing it to come to rest with the ball of your left foot on the ground, the heel raised and your left foot completely empty (1).
• The toes of your left foot should be about two foot lengths forward from your right heel, just left of the centreline of your body. Check your lower leg is perpendicular to the ground (2).

Body work

• Make sure your pelvis is tucked under your spine.

Arm work

• Arc your right hand forwards and upwards, rotating your palm outwards so that the back of your hand is positioned up above your right temple. Your palm should face outwards to the front and right, with your fingers pointing on an angle, upwards and leftwards (1) + (2).
At the same time:
• Sweep your left hand downwards and across your body in much like a 'brush knee' movement so that your left hand finishes out from the side of your left hip, your palm angled downwards and backwards, with your fingers pointing both downwards and forwards (2).

Coordination

- As you start to shift your weight, turn your head to face in the same direction as your body, commence the movement of your arms and begin the forward movement of your left leg.
- Complete the movement of your head, arms and leg simultaneously.

Key points

- Keep your body at the same level while shifting your weight.
- Your entire weight should be on your right leg in the final posture.

Further information

Breathing

- *Breathe in as you bring your hands and leg almost into position.*
- *Breathe out as you settle into the position.*

Chi coordination

Visualise the chi in the heel of your left hand as you bring it down, and in the lao gong point of your right palm as you push it upwards and out-wards. At the end of the move, feel the chi right the way through your spine—from your tailbone up to the bai hui point on your skull.

Common problems with the move

- *The move is quite simple. Most of the problems that arise with it relate to failing to coordinate it properly as well as failing to keep the pelvis tucked under. Also, do not hurry the move—be sure to fully define and experience the posture.*

- *The other main problem is the positioning of the upper hand, which is often held too close to the face, causing the elbow joint to be excessively bent and cutting the flow of chi. It is worthwhile performing the experiment included with the Commencement Movement on page 44 to ensure that you gain the correct hand position.*

Brush Knee and Step Out to Press

Imagery

Imagine fending off a blow to your left side by sweeping your left arm across the side of your body. Follow through with your right palm to push your opponent off balance.

Leg work

• Lift your left knee and Square-Step to the Left (1) (refer page 30).
• Transfer 70 per cent of your weight to your left foot. Your knees should be bent and facing in the same direction as your toes (3).

Body work

• Turn your body 45 degrees to the right (2).
• Turn your body 45 degrees to the left (3).

Arm work

• Rotate your right wrist inwards as you lower your right arm in an arc past your right hip. As your right hand passes your hip your palm faces upwards, fingers pointing forwards. Continue the arc until your hand is extended at shoulder-height, palm facing upwards, fingers pointing away from your body (1) + (2).

At the same time:

• Draw your left hand across your body at waist-height; the heel of your hand leads. Finish the movement with your palm just in front of your right hip, the palm facing downwards with fingers pointing away from your body (2).
• Let the fingers of your right hand lead the hand forwards in a horizontal circle at ear-height back in front of your body where you extend your right hand forwards at heart-height. As you complete this movement, point your fingers upwards, your palm facing forwards (3). (Don't put too much of

a bend in your wrist as this can cut the flow of blood and *chi*. Rather, drop your right elbow to assist your palm in facing forward.) At the same time:

• Draw your left hand leftwards across your body, with the palm down and fingers trailing, to finish at the side of your left hip, the palm angled downwards and backwards, fingers pointing forwards and downwards (3).

Coordination

• Turn your body 90 degrees to the right as you bring your hands into their first position.
• Step out on the square.
• As you transfer your weight forwards, turn your body 90 degrees to the left and bring your hands into their final position.

Key Points

• Keep your upper body erect.

• Turn your spine to bring your arms into position.
• Stepping, brushing and pushing should be done simultaneously.

Further information

Breathing

• *Breathe in as you turn and bring your arms into the first position.*
• *Breathe out as you step forwards and transfer your weight.*

Chi coordination

• *As your left hand clears to the right, visualise the chi in the heel of your left hand. As the right hand is lowered, the chi is in the back of your right hand.*
• *As the left hand clears to the left, visualise the chi in the heel of the left hand. As the right hand presses forwards, visualise the chi extended from the lao gong point in the palm.*

Common problems with the move

• *Waist motion is most important in this move. Keep your arms out from your body and let your waist provide most of the movement. Focus on keeping your arms curved, with your elbows and armpits open.*
• *When you bring your right hand forwards, lead with your fingers and not with your palm. Leading with the palm creates an unnatural constriction in the flow of chi and blood at the wrist. It can also cause lifting in the shoulder. Your palm should only come to face forwards at the end of the move, and this is achieved by dropping the elbow, not bending the wrist.*

Play the Lute

Also known as Strumming the Lute

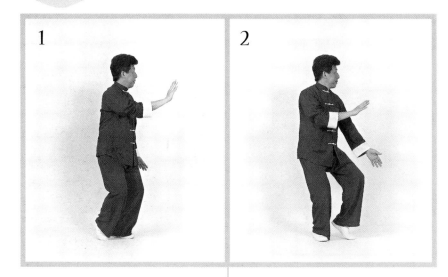

Imagery
Refer to Level 1 Play the Lute, page 62.

Leg work
• Transfer your weight to your left foot. Then bring the instep of your right foot in a few centimetres behind the heel of your left foot, placing it at a **45** degree angle (1).
• Transfer all your weight to your right foot.
• Raise your left knee to lift your left foot and place it comfortably in front of you– your heel resting on the floor, toes raised. Check your right knee is bent, with your lower left leg making an angle of about 45 degrees to the ground. There should be no weight on your left foot (4).

Body work
• Turn your body slightly to the right.
• Turn your body slightly to the left.

Arm work
• Relax your right wrist and draw your right hand downwards to around about heart-height. Your palm should be angled downwards and leftwards, with your fingers pointing forwards.
At the same time:
• Relax your left wrist so that your fingers point downwards.
• Arc your left hand upwards until it comes to rest at about chest height, opposite the centreline of your body. Your palm should face to the right, with your fingers angled upwards (3).
• Check your left hand is extended suffi-ciently in front of your body to prevent any closure of your elbow or armpit, but not so far as to lift your shoulder or straighten the elbow joint. Your right palm faces the inside of your left elbow (4).

Coordination

- Transfer your weight to your left foot and step up with your right foot as you relax both hands and commence the arm movements.
- Transfer your weight to your right foot, turn your body to the right as you draw your right hand down and take your left hand upwards and raise your left knee.
- Lower your left and right hands into position as you turn your body to the left and lower your left leg.

Key points

- The half step (to step up behind the left foot) should be light.
- Keep your centre of gravity moving smoothly and at the same level.
- Your whole weight should be on your right leg in the final posture.

- The final placement of your hands and feet should be completed simultaneously.

Further information

Breathing
- *Breathe in as you step up and raise your left leg.*
- *Breathe out as you lower your hands and left leg into position.*

Chi coordination
Refer to Level 1 Play the Lute, page 63.

Common problems with the move
Refer to Level 1 Play the Lute, page 63.

Double Block and Slant Flying

Imagery

For the Double Block, imagine looking behind and using both of your arms to fend off an attacker. For Slant Flying, imagine spreading your arms as if in flight.

Leg work

• Turn your left foot 45 degrees to the right and relax it to the ground.

• Step into a Left-foot Square Stance (page 26) and transfer 70 per cent of your weight to your left foot.

Body work

• Turn your body 45 degrees to the right.

• Turn your body 45 degrees to the left.

Arm work

• Rotate your right hand slightly inwards so that your palm faces towards your chest.

• Now arc your left hand downwards across the front of your body until it finishes opposite your right hip. Check that your palm faces downwards, and your fingers point outwards (1).

At the same time:

• Arc your right hand upwards across the front of your body to the right and then downwards to the right, finishing with your palm angled downwards and forwards, at heart height, to the right of your body. The fingers of both hands point slightly up and away to the right of your body. (If you could trace the pattern of the movement in the air it would be similar to that of two windscreen wipers, with the right wiper moving after the left.) This completes the Double Block part of the move (1).

• Rotate your left hand outwards to turn your palm slightly upwards (2).

3

• Arc your right hand horizontally forwards until it crosses under your left forearm (2).
• Sweep your right hand downwards in a clearing motion, brush over your right leg and finish at the side of your right hip. Check your palm is angled downwards and backwards, with fingers pointing forwards and downwards (3).
At the same time:
• Arc your left hand forwards, outwards and upwards to finish with your arm extended, your left hand at shoulder-height. Check your palm faces upwards, and your fingers point forwards and slightly to the left (3).

Coordination

• Turn your body to the right as you Double Block.
• Turn your body to the left as you prepare for the Slant Flying and place your left foot.

• Transfer your weight as you continue the body motion to the left, clearing down and Slant Flying.

Key points

• In the Double Block, keep the centre of gravity over your right leg.
• Keep your upper body erect while turning.
• Keep your body at the same level during the transfer of weight.
• Your eyes should follow your right hand during the block.
• In Slant Flying, the motion of your arms should follow your turning body.
• The motion of your arms, the turning of your body and the transfer of weight should be completed simultaneously.

Further information

Breathing
• Breathe in as you take your left hand over.
• Breathe out as you take your right hand over.
• Breathe in as you prepare for Slant Flying.
• Breathe out as you transfer your weight and complete Slant Flying.

Chi coordination
Visualise the chi being expressed from the lao gong points of your palms. Also, you should visualise the chi sinking downwards through the yong quan point of your feet.

Common problems with the move
• Hands and arms too close to the body, blocking the flow of blood and chi. Allow your waist to generate most of the movements.

Cross Deflection, Kick and Thrust

1

2

Imagery

For the Cross Deflection, imagine striking downwards on an opponent's head with a reverse fist (knuckles down).

For the Kick and Thrust, imagine thrusting your left palm, like a spearhead, directly at your opponent's throat, while simultaneously kicking at your opponent's shin with your right foot.

Leg work

• Transfer 70 per cent of your weight to your right foot.
• Lift the ball of your left foot and open out to an angle of 45 degrees. Transfer 100 per cent of your weight to your left foot.
• Raise your right knee to about waist-height, then extend your right foot forwards, turning your right heel inwards and your toes outwards.

Body work

• Turn your body 45 degrees to the left.
• Turn your body 45 degrees to the right.

Arm work

• Form your right hand into a cotton fist (see page 76). Rotate your hand inwards and arc it up across the front of your body to heart height (1).
At the same time:
• Rotate your left hand inwards and drop your left elbow so that your left palm is angled forwards, fingers pointing outwards.
• Draw your left hand downwards to bring it in front of the centreline of your body at chest height. Check your left hand is some-what to the front of your right hand (1).
• Continue clearing down with your left hand to *tan tien* (abdomen) height.
At the same time:

- Rotating through your right elbow, arc your right hand forwards and downwards. If your fist were uncurled your palm would face up, fingers pointing forwards.
- As your right fist comes down, move your left hand slightly upwards so that your downward facing left palm comes up over the inside of the elbow of your right arm (2).
- Pull your right hand back to the side of your right hip. Your hand should still be in a cotton fist, your knuckles facing forwards (4). At the same time:
- Push your left hand forwards and upwards to neck-height in front of the centre of your body, your arm in a soft curve. Check your hand is angled to the right, your palm facing downwards, fingers pointing forwards (4).

Coordination

- Transfer your weight to your back foot as

you turn to the left and bring your right hand into the position to clear.
- Transfer your weight to the front foot as you clear down and turn to the right.
- Bring your left hand and right knee into position for the Kick and Thrust.
- Kick with your right leg as you thrust with your left hand and draw your cotton fist into your hip.

Key points

- In the deflection, press down with your left palm first, closely followed by the punch with your right fist.
- Make sure you keep your body upright, particularly in the downward deflection.
- Withdrawing with the right fist, thrusting with the left palm and kicking out with the right foot should all be completed at the same time.

Cross Deflection, Kick and Thrust continued

Further information

Breathing
- Breathe in as you deflect.
- Breathe out as you kick and thrust.

Chi coordination
Visualise the chi being expressed from the lao gong point in the palm of your left hand as it clears down and from the back of your right hand during the downward deflection. In the kick and thrust, the chi is expressed from the yong quan point in the soles of both the kicking and supporting foot, as well as in the fingers of the left hand.

Common problems with the move
- Remember to clear down with the left hand and have the fist follow the clearing pattern.
- There are some common problems with the fist being held too tight and the kick being too vigorous but these are dealt with in the section on Tai Chi fists below.
- Perhaps the major problem when kicking is balance. Sinking into the left foot and not kicking too high or too fast should resolve this. Practising the flow pattern will also help.
- Make sure you don't unduly bend your right elbow when drawing the fist back to the side.

Tai Chi kicks
This is the first kick encountered in the Tai Chi set. Resist the temptation to become overly dramatic; the kick should be slow and controlled. The concept of 'mian' (or silk-like movement) should be applied to the leg as well as to the arm extensions. This means you should slow

the kick before it reaches its full extension. Do not straighten your leg.

In a real kick, straightening the leg would never occur as the momentum that you are seeking to flow out of your foot is turned back on the knee joint. Far better in 'shadow' kicks that this momentum be absorbed by the flexor muscles of the leg rather than the knee ligaments and cartilage.

A kick is different to a step (be it full or empty) in that the objective is to flow chi out through the foot. Each kick in the Tai Chi set is different. In this kick the focus is on flowing chi out of the centre part of the sole of the foot, not the heel or toes.

Tai Chi fists
This move is also the first time where we encounter the closed fist in Tai Chi. It should be remembered that Tai Chi utilises the 'cotton fist' – that is, the fist is held as though holding a small bird's egg within it. This helps to avoid putting too much tension within the fist.

Compare for yourself the whiteness of the skin of your hand when you form a fist where your fingers are dug into the centre of the palm. This whiteness indicates that the flow of blood, and thus of chi, is being constricted and this is to be avoided.

Parry

Imagery

Imagine fending off attackers with your left palm.

Leg work

• Gently lower your right foot to the ground, heel first, drawing it in towards your body. Check your right heel is in line with your left heel.

• As you bring your toes to the ground, make sure that they are turned outwards 45 degrees. (You can turn them more than this but you will then need to adjust position when you Square Step to the Left.)

At the same time:

• Shift the weight of your left foot onto the ball of your left foot, raise your left heel and bring your left knee in behind your right knee. All of your weight should be on your right foot.

Body work

• Turn your waist 45 degrees to the right.

Arm work

• Slightly drop the elbow and wrist of your left hand so that your palm now faces rightwards. Check your fingers point upwards, the little finger edge of the hand faces forwards and your shoulders and elbows are relaxed.

Coordination

• Bring your right foot down and position your left hand as you push your weight forwards, raising your left heel and 'slotting in' with your left knee.

Key points

• Place your right foot on the floor and turn your upper body at the same time.
• Keep your upper body erect.
• Keep your shoulders and elbows relaxed and down.

Further information

Breathing

• Breathe in as you lower your foot.
• Breathe out as you transfer your weight.

Chi coordination

Visualise the chi in the leading edge of your left palm, just below your little finger. You should also visualise the chi moving downwards through the yong quan point of your right foot.

Punch

Often referred to as Punch to Heart

Imagery

Imagine using your back foot in order to propel your body forwards, and thrusting your fist forwards to punch.

Leg work

• Square Step to the Left (page 30) with your left foot (1).
• Transfer 70 per cent of your weight to your left foot (2). (If you opened your right foot wider than 45 degrees in the Parry then you will need to adjust it.)

Body work

• Turn your body 45 degrees to the left.

Arm work

• Push your right fist forwards, rotating your wrist inwards 90 degrees as you do so. The punch finishes immediately in front of the heart of your imagined opponent, with the right arm extended but not straight. If the fist was opened, the palm would naturally face left (2).

At the same time:

• Move your left hand back slightly so that your left palm faces the inside of your right elbow, palm facing rightwards and fingers pointing upwards.

Coordination

• Step. As you transfer the weight forwards, push your right fist forwards and bring your left hand back to guard.

Key points

• The transfer of the weight and punching of the fist should be completed simultaneously.
• Do not shrug your shoulders and raise your elbows.

Further information

Breathing
- *Breathe in as you step.*
- *Breathe out as you transfer your weight and punch.*

Chi coordination
While the movement is a punch, it should not be violent or excessively stressed. There should, however, be a sensation of conscious control of the fist. Feel (or imagine) the chi in the knuckles of the fist and directed forwards.

Common problems with the move
- *Straightening the arm with the punch and failing to rotate the wrist are the two common problems. The power of the punch is generated from the legs and directed through the waist.*

Extend Arms to Push

Also known as Push to Close the Door

Imagery

For the last half of this movement, imagine that you are pushing to close a heavy door, such as you might see in an old temple or church.

Leg work

- Transfer 70 per cent of your weight to your right foot (2).
- Transfer 70 per cent of your weight to your left foot (4).

Body work

- There is a very slight rightwards movement of your body as you draw back.
- There is a leftwards movement of your body as you move forwards, so that, at the completion of the move, you face forwards (so that you are facing directly over the toes of your supporting foot).

Arm work

- Open your right fist and rotate your palm so that it faces upwards (1).

At the same time:

- Rotate your left hand and turn your left palm to face upwards, positioned under your right forearm.
- Draw your hand back through your right elbow. Rotate both palms until they are facing forwards, at about heart-height (3).
- Arc both your hands forwards and upwards to about chest-height. Your elbows should be dropped, allowing your palms to face forwards without bending your wrists. Your hands should remain shoulder-width apart (4).

Coordination

- Prepare your hands.
- As you transfer your weight into your

right foot, turn your body and draw back through your right elbow (2).

• As you turn your body back, rotate your palms (3).

• As you transfer your weight back to your left foot, push your hands forwards to chest-height (4).

• At the end of this movement check that your knees are bent but facing in the same direction as your toes, your arms are in gentle curves, and your armpits and the inside of your elbow joints are open.

Key points

• Keep your upper body upright and slightly turned rightwards while your upper body is settling back.

• Pushing your palms forwards and transferring your weight should be completed simultaneously.

Further information

Breathing

• Breathe in as you transfer your weight to your right foot.

• Breathe out as you transfer your weight to your left foot.

Chi coordination

Visualise the chi being expressed through the lao gong points in both palms as your hands push forwards and upwards.

Common problems with the move

Refer to Push to Close the Door, page 54.

Cross Hands

Imagery

Imagine the branches of a willow blowing in the breeze—in this movement your arms become like the branches of a willow blowing in a breeze, very fluid and light. (In the body, the breeze is the flow of *chi*.) The spirit at the completion of the move is that of a sage repelling a pouncing tiger. The sage is calm, without a desire to injure. There is a feeling of strength and expanding power, as though a wave of energy were surging slowly but powerfully out of your body, such that the tiger would be effortlessly repelled.

Leg work

• Transfer all of your weight to your right foot. Complete by lifting the ball of your left foot (1).

• Turn your left toes inwards 90 degrees and let your foot relax to the ground.

• Transfer all your weight to your left foot.

• Raise your right heel, letting your foot pivot leftwards then rightwards (3).

• Lift your right knee and step out to the Shoulder-width Stance.

• Transfer 50 per cent of your weight to your right foot. Refer to Chapter 3, page 29, for details on stepping to the side.

Body work

• Turn your body 90 degrees to the right (2).

• Turn your body 90 degrees to the left (4).

• Turn your body 45 degrees to the right (6).

Arm work

• Relax both wrists.

• Turn your right elbow out slightly so that your right palm is angled to the right, your fingers pointing forwards. Make sure that while your palm is higher than your shoulder,

your elbow is actually lower (2).
At the same time:

• Arc your left hand downwards to hip-height, rotating your hand so that your palm is angled to the right with fingers pointing forwards (2).

Once the body movement has carried your arms as far rightwards as comfortable:

• Arc your right hand downwards to hip-height. Your palm should be angled outwards, your fingers pointing rightwards (4).

At the same time:

• Rotate your left hand inwards and raise your left hand to shoulder-height, keeping your elbow dropped. Check your palm faces your body, your fingers angled upwards and rightwards (4).

Once the body movement has carried your arms as far leftwards as they can comfortably reach:

• Rotate your right hand inwards and drop your right elbow, so that you cross hands at the wrists, the front of your left wrist resting on the back of your right wrist. Check the crossed wrists are at face-height, directly in front of the centreline of your body, palms facing your body (4).

• Keeping your wrists in contact, rotate your wrists outwards and slightly upwards so that the 'little finger' edge of your left wrist is pressing against the 'thumb' edge of your right wrist (5).

• The fingers continue to be extended upwards at an angle (6).

Coordination

• Let your hands come into position as you draw your weight back to your right foot.

• Turn your body to the right and bring your left foot around to the front. It will appear as

though your arms are being swept rightwards but this is because of the turning motion of your body (3).

- Turn your body to the left, raising your right heel and transferring all the weight into your left foot (4).
- Turn your body back to the front and place your right foot in the Shoulder-width Stance. Centre your crossed hands and equalise your weight on both feet (6).

Key points

- Keep your body upright.
- Keep your shoulders relaxed and your elbows down.
- Both of your arms should be slightly extended to create a circle.
- Keep your pelvis tucked under and your shoulders down at the completion of the movement.

Further information

Breathing

- *Breathe in as you transfer your weight back and position your arms.*
- *Breathe out as you turn your body to the right.*
- *Breathe in as you turn your body to the left.*
- *Breathe out as you settle into the Shoulder-width Stance, roll your hands and block upwards.*

Chi coordination

- *When taking all the weight into your left foot and stepping to the parallel stance (the Shoulder-width Stance), visualise the chi moving down through the yong quan point in your left foot. Visualise the chi being expressed from the lao gong points of your hands when your palms face in the direction of movement, and in backs of your hands when they face the direction of* movement. At the completion of the movement focus on the chi in the leading edge of your hands. The movement should be very 'strong', though not tense.

Common problems with the move

- Do not draw your arms in too close to your body if the framework of this move is to remain strong. Keep your body upright when stepping to the right.
- Make sure that your fingers do not curl at the completion of the move. Strength can be added by sinking slightly as your hands block up. This sinking is not particularly visible and is more 'mind intent', to provide a firm, rooting sensation for the feet that will give the whole posture strength.
- Another vital element in the strength of the movement is keeping your back straight and your pelvis properly tucked forwards.

Special note

- On page 33 the subject of the avoidance of double weightedness was introduced and it was pointed out that this Tai Chi principle was not breached as long as there was a separation of yin and yang by pushing downwards through the legs while the upper part of the body directed force upward and outwards through the crossed hands. Now that we have completed all of the actual Tai Chi movements contained within the sequence taught in this book, it is worthwhile contemplating a little more deeply what this principle of avoiding double weightedness actually teaches us.

Most Chi Kung exercises (chi means skill with energy—and in this sense Tai Chi is a Chi Kung

exercise) have the body weight equally spread over both feet either for part or all of the time, so why should the ancient Tai Chi masters see double weightedness as such a potential problem? In the Tai Chi Ching Classics (instructions by the ancient Tai Chi masters as to the principles to be embodied within Tai Chi) there are constant injunctions to 'Flow like a great river' and ensure that 'When one part of the body moves all parts of the body move'. These instructions are really all dealing with the dangers of letting the chi of the body separate. The whole point of the Tai Chi exercise is to use the body so that the chi is focussed and acting as one. Not only does this have significant martial art application, it means that the energy of the body, mind, spirit and emotion can be focussed in a unified manner on any goal or activity in life. This achieves great power.

To achieve this we need to understand the distinction between maintaining one chi but separating yin and yang. An analogy may help here. Think of chi as an electric current. This current must be unified and regular if it is to operate machinery efficiently and effectively. However, the positive and negative electrical flows within the current must remain separate, and the more powerful and balanced these individual flows, the stronger the overall current. Fully appreciating the subtleties of this principle may take years, but it is a principle worth understanding and reflecting on. Once it is understood and applied, one's health and quality of life can be greatly improved. It is one of the great secrets that Tai Chi has to teach us.

Closing Movement

In practice the Khor-style Tai Chi form would now continue on from the Cross Hands movement, but it marks the end of Level 2 and, thus, the completion of our movements for the time being.

So, to close the set:
• Roll both of your hands inwards until your palms are angled downwards.
• Extending slightly through your hands, slide your left palm over the back of your right hand and separate your hands until they are shoulder-width apart (1).
• Relaxing down through your shoulders and elbows, gently push your palms downwards to the side of your hips, as if you had a balloon under each palm (2).
• Allow your body to relax and become still and then complete with the Formal Closing Movement.

Further information

Breathing
• Breathe in as you extend your arms.
• Breathe out as you lower your arms and relax.

Chi coordination
As you raise your hands and bring them in, imagine that you are gathering chi. As you bring them down, imagine sinking the chi down to the tan tien (abdomen).

Common problems with the move
• Finishing too quickly, rushing the movement. Take your time and feel the chi, maintaining the same tempo as for the previous movements.
• Make sure you take three relaxed breaths at the end of the movement.

Formal Closing Movement

To formally close the set:
- Draw your hands to hip height whilst sinking your weight and transferring your weight to your right leg. Draw back your elbows, rotating your hands so your palms face upwards with fingers pointing forwards.
- As you complete the weight transfer, arc your hands outwards and upwards until they are extended at shoulder-height, fingers pointing to the sides.
- Lift your left knee and bring your left foot into the side of your right foot, with the toes of both feet pointing forwards. At the same time, drop your elbows so that your hands rise up to face-height, arcing your hands in towards your body until they are shoulder-width apart, palms facing downwards, fingers pointing forwards, and transfer your weight equally into both feet
- Rise to the knee off-lock position while

lowering your elbows to bring your palms down to the sides of the body, with your palms facing inwards, fingers pointing down, armpits open.

Key points
- Keep your spine straight.
- Keep your movement slow and fluid.

Further information

Breathing
- Breathe in as you raise your arms and shift your weight to your right foot.
- Breathe out as you relax your chest and straighten your body back to normal height.
- Take several calming breaths.

Note: Refer also to the Further information given on page 86.

CHAPTER 5

Tai Chi for Life

Life's main arenas

We must remember that life is made up of related, not isolated, activities—change the balance in one area of your life, and the effects spill over into the other areas, which in turn impact on others. For thousands of years the Chinese people have focussed on certain major areas of life. By keeping these areas under observation ourselves, we have a reference point from which to judge the impact of Tai Chi on our own lives.

The areas of life I am speaking about are related to the directions on the Bagua (which refers to the eight trigrams of the *I Ching*, the *Book of Changes*), as used in Feng Shui. This is not a coincidence—both arts are concerned with balancing and harmonising *chi* and have, as their roots, the same basic philosophy of achieving a balance between *yin* and *yang* energies. The order of areas—which include health, wealth, career, knowledge, relationship, fame, children and benefactors—is here grouped slightly differently from the Bagua.

Health

Health is not merely the absence of physical disease, but reflects the all-round state of your body, including its physical, mental, emotional and energetic aspects. It is interesting to note that Western medicine looks to providing a cure for illness once the symptoms have appeared, whereas Chinese medicine aims to prevent illness from occurring. 'Prescribing' Tai Chi is one of those preventive methods of Chinese medicine, due to its tremendous impact on internal bodily function.

How our bodies respond to stimuli is a crucial factor of their programming and, hence, health. The body operates in one of two modes, either the relaxation response or the stress response.

Relaxation response

When your body is in the relaxation response, it is operating in long-term survival mode, at optimum performance in order to last your full life span. The practice of Tai Chi is one way of obtaining extended time in this mode. The benefits accrued from spending increased time spent in the relaxation response include:

1. An increase in the supply of blood, and therefore oxygen and nutrients, to your internal organs, as well as increased efficiency in the removal of wastes and toxins.
2. Better functioning of your digestive system. When stressed, your body suppresses its production of various gastric juices and the absorption of some key vitamins is adversely affected.
3. An increase in resistance to disease and infection, due to the optimal functioning of your immune system.
4. A reduced chance of injury from falls and accidents, relating to the removal of tension from your muscles, increased muscle tone and joint flexibility, together with better neurological coordination. (Studies show Tai Chi practitioners are less prone to falls.)
5. Increased breathing efficiency, resulting in heightened physical energy, less fatigue and a sense of vitality. Also aids in the management of conditions such as asthma and emphysema.

6. Improved posture, which helps to alleviate back problems, and also encourages a more positive mental outlook.

7. An increased internal massaging effect, improving the blood supply to your internal organs, thereby allowing them to operate more effectively. This includes those organs involved with digestive and eliminatory functions.

8. Improved cardiovascular efficiency, which aids the heart and circulatory system. Slower, deeper breathing reduces the number of heart contractions per quantity of blood circulated, thus reducing the demands on your heart.

9. An increased flow of *chi*, which can help virtually any body function and resolve many problems.

10. Increased left-brain functioning, which improves your memory, ability to concentrate and willpower.

11. Increased right-brain functioning, which improves your emotional balance and control, intuition and creative abilities. Tai Chi helps you to create a more positive outlook and dispel depression.

Stress response

The stress response is your body's short-term survival mode, providing defence mechanisms designed to cope with an emergency. When your body is in this mode, blood withdraws from your internal organs, is directed to the muscles, and is thickened to reduce the amount lost in case of injury; your hormone levels increase (to enable the maximum metabolic response); and your heart rate goes up. Basically, they are the reactions that are the complete opposite of when your body is in the relaxation response.

There is, of course, nothing wrong with the stress response, and we are all extremely grateful for it when an emergency arises. The problem lies, however, not in the response itself but in our modern, high-pressure world that continually triggers it in us unnecessarily. When a stimulus triggering the stress response does not require a physical reaction to remove it, then without that physical reaction your body finds it difficult to release the stress and move back into the relaxation response. When you are in stress response unnecessarily, your body expends significant amounts of energy and suffers long-term damage for no benefit.

Practising Tai Chi not only provides a means of moving from stress response to relaxation response during the actual performance of the movements, it also dissipates accumulated muscular tension and trains your body to move out of stress response more easily and at any time.

The individual benefits to be gained from the relaxation response are quite considerable. When combined, they provide another very important aspect: with all of these improvements, your body now takes less energy to run than previously. This surplus energy is then available to you to be invested into other areas of your life, with very positive results.

Family and relationships

After our personal health, our most important asset is our relationships—not only those within the family but with friends, work mates, etc. With more energy (and less stress and tension), you will be better able to deal with the people around you in a positive and understanding manner.

Being in a relaxed state will give you the energy to help you to be patient and to listen with understanding, whereas tiredness and tension tend to breed short temperedness and abruptness. Increased energy will make you want to participate in activities with others, whereas before you were simply too tired. The improved way in which you deal with others will now strengthen those relationships, rather than create conflict.

This, in turn, has the effect of freeing up even more energy—energy previously employed in tension and conflict—together with the increase in energy generated through warmer and more supporting relationships.

Tai Chi is far more than a simple exercise set—it is a way of thinking. Mind and body become better interlinked, and changing the way you move affects the way you think: the lessons that your mind has learnt about balance and harmony on a physical plane will unconsciously be applied on mental levels. Don't be surprised to get comments about 'how much easier you are to deal with'.

A final influence on relationships, not to be overlooked, arises out of the more positive mental attitude the practice of Tai Chi engenders.

People like to be associated with a positive, optimistic person, and so any movement you make in this direction will increase both the quantity and quality of your relationships.

Creativity and children

This is a highly interesting combination, reflecting the Chinese view that the realisation of a child's full potential requires all the imagination and all the creativity of the most demanding artistic activity. The nature of artistic creation and the raising of children are, therefore, seen as very similar endeavours.

Again, the increased energy and positivism resulting from the practice of Tai Chi, and the adoption of Tai Chi principles, enhance creativity and, thus in this sense, the raising of children. The ability to flow your body smoothly and easily from one posture to another reproduces itself in your ability to flow through emotional states more easily, while visualisation techniques free up your imagination.

In the raising of children there is a constant requirement to empathise, to be able to see the world from a child's perspective and to understand a child's emotions and feelings. This takes all the energy, flexibility and imagination you will ever possess.

Helpful people

Success in life is often built upon the help we receive from others (often referred to as networking). If you are relaxed, energetic, enthusiastic and able to relate to people more effectively, then you are more likely to receive their help and assistance.

Wealth and prosperity

It may be difficult to see just how Tai Chi will benefit your life in this area, but it does not take a great stretch of imagination to see how having more energy to commit to your business can lead to an increase in wealth. A clear-thinking and healthy existence also helps to reduce expenditure. A positive approach to life can lead to better identifying opportunities and having the energy to take advantage of them.

Career and travel

If you can approach your career in a more relaxed and positive fashion, have more energy to expend in this arena and your working relationships are improving, then the chance of promotion and increased remuneration (or, if self-employed, increased volume of business) is greatly enhanced.

With improvements in your health, career and business, relationships, networking and wealth, then the more the opportunity for travel can open up in your life.

Fame and recognition

Fame and recognition are not simply a matter of ego. Your reputation can be important for advancement in your career or business, or artistically. It is an interesting fact that the type of characteristics developed from practices such as Tai Chi are those often admired. There is more chance of recognition when you are performing well, your networking is improving and your relationships with people are good.

Knowledge and intuition

A relaxed mind is a more perceptive mind. The energy to study leads to the opportunity to acquire new knowledge and perspective, enhances your ability to take advantage of your intuition and to identify the life that you truly want to lead.

Tai Chi, then, can benefit every aspect of your life. In essence, what Tai Chi does is add a positive feedback effect to your life.

Practices complementary to Tai Chi

Tai Chi is based both on a philosophy of life and an understanding of how the energy called *chi* operates. Your study and practice of Tai Chi can open up many opportunities to extend this understanding and obtain its optimum benefits.

Tai Chi primarily focuses on the balancing and harmonisation of your bodily *chi*. It also works on increasing the flow of *chi* that occurs during respiration as the air flows into and out of your body. As you become more aware of *chi*, there usually comes an expanding desire to know more about this subtle energy and the role that it plays in life. There are a number of other Chinese practices which can be used to complement your understanding of *chi* through Tai Chi.

Chi nutrition

Chi nutrition is concerned with ensuring that your diet results in the optimum quantity and quality of *chi* being taken into the body during the digestive process. This includes:

- Eating the right quantity of food.
- Eating the right mix of foods (with the right mix of *chi*) appropriate to your body and lifestyle.
- Identifying good quality food which has been correctly stored and packaged so as to preserve *chi*.
- Observing proper cooking procedures to preserve and enhance the *chi* content of the food.
- Ensuring the pleasing presentation of food, to stimulate your digestion and enhance *chi* absorption.
- Observing correct eating techniques, to maximise *chi* absorption.
- Utilising suitable eating environments for eating to enhance *chi* absorption.

Feng Shui

Feng Shui (literal translation: *feng*, 'wind' and *shui*, 'water') is a series of techniques for analysing our environment so that we can make the necessary adjustments in order to maximise the environmental flow of *chi*. This has the ripple effect of heightening your personal *chi* flow.

Mind Power Chi Kung

Chi Kung means energy skill or energy art. Mind power Chi Kung is a way of strengthening the *chi* of your mind through physical and mental exercise, including meditation, visualisation, affirmation and positive thinking techniques.

Acupressure and Acumassage

These techniques improve the flow of *chi* and remove *chi* blockages that might otherwise result in illness.

Chi Kung

This includes techniques such as Tao Yin (an energy art that uses breathing and stretching movements to cultivate *chi* energy and good health). Such techniques supplement Tai Chi by providing exercises for the stimulation of *chi* flow to a greater extent than is possible (over the short term) with Tai Chi.

How to introduce Tai Chi into your daily life

Whether you have tried some of the Tai Chi movements or are still in the throes of simply reading the book, you must be starting to feel a little absorbed by the wonder of Tai Chi. Perhaps you are intrigued by Tai Chi's ancientness? Tai Chi has only been popularised in the West during the last 30 years or so and, although most know the word, the majority of people are still unaware of its complex history and the centuries it has taken to reach us—hundreds of years of trial, growth and increasing understanding. It is said that there is a time for everything—maybe Tai Chi has been given to us now, in an era when it is more than needed.

Perhaps you are a little daunted by the descriptions and pictures? Tai Chi is not just about movements. Tai Chi needs to be felt, so let me try to pass on some of that feeling.

Feeling Tai Chi

Turn to the movement called Commencement Movement, at page 44. For the moment, do not be overly concerned with any of the technicalities—just make sure you have a reasonable idea of the movement's shape. Read the movement's imagery and apply this visualisation during your performance; turn it into a flow pattern by simply performing one Commencement Movement after another. Put on some gentle, relaxing music. Breathe naturally and let the movement follow your breathing pattern—your hands floating up as you breathe in and coming down as you breathe out. This movement is often called 'Floating Hands', and floating is the key word. Don't 'try' to do the movement, just allow your whole mind and body to become absorbed in it. Repeat it as many times as you feel comfortable—usually about 20 repetitions will find you entering the relaxation response. Just this one movement will produce an incredible reaction inside your body.

You have just discovered that it does not take forever to learn anything about Tai Chi. Once you have become aware of the relaxation response, there are other ways to help initiate it. When you get up in the morning, do some gentle stretching, followed by the Commencement Movement flow pattern. This has the wonderful effect of stirring and warming-up your body, energising and preparing it for the day ahead.

If you have a sedentary job, make sure you get up from your chair every hour and stretch, or go for a walk. If you spend many hours at a computer, rest your eyes every so often by looking away from the screen and into the distance. Go for a walk at lunchtime, or eat your lunch in a nearby park. Find a quiet space for a few minutes' meditation, or practise your Tai Chi. Many people suffer from what we call 'afternoon slump'. Again, stretch, take a short walk and try and get some fresh air. This is not the time to partake of chocolate or a fizzy drink—it will leave you feeling worse, usually at the time when you need to be fresh to spend time with your family or to enjoy evening activities.

Contrary to what you may think, television is not a relaxant. If it is used correctly it can be a great tool, but all too often it is a babysitter or a means of nullifying the mind. Turn it off, play a game with your children, take your dog for a walk.

All of these are Tai Chi-like activities—they act as a means of relieving stress and tension and aid in the *chi*-balancing process.

Where to from here?

Start by bringing some of the above small changes into your life: learn the movements outlined in this book and practise them regularly. Tai Chi will repay you by taking you on a journey into a new world. Those words might sound a little far-fetched to you at the moment, but hundreds of thousands of Tai Chi people (plus the billions in China) cannot be wrong.

Tai Chi is a tool, not a master—taking you only in the direction you wish to go, at the speed you wish to travel—but it will show you much along the way. Many practitioners say that Tai Chi is like an old friend— you can take it with you through the whole of your life and it is always there when you need it. After many years of devoted practice it is still as fresh and exciting as it was on the first encounter, even for someone like myself, whose life has been mostly dedicated to Tai Chi.

This book contains about one third of the full Khor Tai Chi form. I hope you go on to learn the remainder, but even if you perform what you have learnt in this book for three or more 20-minute periods a week, then you can expect 90 per cent of the benefits that you would get from the physical practice of the full Tai Chi set. Although to learn the full form is a fascinating journey in itself, the main secret to Tai Chi lies not in more moves or forms, but in deeper knowledge and understanding of the movements you are performing. The benefits come from the doing of Tai Chi not the learning of Tai Chi. A Chinese Grandmaster once said to me:

> During my life I learned over 150 forms. Of these I have completely forgotten over 100; of the remaining 50, I can perform only some of the moves from each form, managing 12 forms with some proficiency; of these 12 forms I feel I have come close to mastering three. If I had my time all over again, I would spend it all on these three—the others were just a distraction.

This does not mean that you should not explore related arts and disciplines, but keep what you have learned as your foundation, maintaining and building on it, rather than rushing off to build another half-structure.

The end of this book marks the beginning of your Tai Chi journey, not the end of it. The Chinese say that a journey of 1000 miles begins with the first step—may this be your first step towards a life of health, peace and happiness.

Contacts

Australia

Australian Academy of Tai Chi
www.livingchi.com.au

STATE OFFICES
New South Wales (National Head Office)
PO Box 1020
Burwood North NSW 2134
Tel/Fax: (02) 9797 9355

Queensland
PO Box 2475
BC Qld 4006
Tel: (07) 3358 1955

South Australia
GPO Box 1306
Adelaide SA 5001
Tel: (08) 8287 3571

Tasmania
PO Box 1688
Launceston TAS 7250
Tel: (03) 6362 3428

REGIONAL OFFICES
New South Wales

Albury/Corowra	(02) 6033 3172
Baradine	(02) 6843 1982
Central Coast	(02) 4332 7176
Coonabarabran	(02) 6842 2079
Kootingal	(02) 6765 8292
Newcastle	(02) 4942 2951
Orange	(02) 6365 8309
Tamworth	(02) 6766 6706
Woollongong	(02) 4261 5786

Queensland

Bundaberg	(07) 4153 4428
Gold Coast	(07) 5572 8921
Gympie	(07) 5486 5131
Rockhampton	(07) 4939 5845
Sunshine Coast	(07) 5491 2314
Toowoomba	(07) 4636 5034

New Zealand

Auckland
New Zealand Martial Arts Council
PO Box 6971, Wellesley Street
Tel: (09) 309 2855

Tai Chi Academy
Milford and Mt Eden
Tel: (09) 489 8348

Sing Ong Tai Chi
678 Mt Albert Road, Royal Oak
Tel: (09) 625 8833
Website: www.singongtaichi.com
Can put you in contact with associated
organisations throughout the North Island.

Tai Chi Aotearoa
40 St Benedicts Street, Newton
Tel: (09) 376 9074
Website: www.taichi.co.nz
Also has contact with Dunedin groups

Christchurch
Chan's Martial Arts Headquarters
15 Lawson Street, Sydenham
Tel: (03) 366 0791

Most university recreation centres have Tai
Chi classes. Details from individual centres.

United Kingdom

Taoist Tai Chi Society — European Federation
Taoist Tai Chi Centre (Colchester)
Tel: 01206 576 167
Fax: 01206 572 269
Email: europe@taoist.org

The British Council for Chinese Martial Arts
(Warwickshire)
Tel/fax: 01203 394642
Website: www.bccma.org.uk
Large amount of members, including most of
the UK's major martial arts organisations.
Website has links to all its members' sites.

The Tai Chi Union for Great Britain (Glasgow)
Tel: 0141 638 2946
Fax: 0141 621 1220
Email: secretary@taichiunion.com.uk
Largest collective of instuctors in the UK.
Can help you find a local teacher.

SCHOOLS:
Chen Style Tai Chi Centre (Manchester)
Contact: Li-Ming Yue
Tel: 0161 274 4967 (Home) or
0161 228 3113 (Work and Fax)
Email: TaiChiClub@aol.com

The James Uglow Tai Chi School (Essex)
Tel: 0836 665509
Email: info@taichi.co.uk

Mountain River Tai Chi Club
Tel: 07957 322 036
Website: www.mountainriver.co.uk
Regular classes across London (Chiswick,
Hammersmith, Teddington, Wimbledon).
Private tuition available by arrangement.

Rising Dragon Tai Chi School (Worcester)
Tel/fax: 01905 764848
Email: alan@rdtcschool.freeserve.co.uk

The Sunswallow School of Tai Chi and Qi
Gong (Worcestershire)
Tel: 01299 825868
Email: sunswallow@hotmail.com
Classes in Gloucester, Worcester and the
West Midlands.

South Africa

Cape Town
Tai Chi Institute of Health Centres

Durbanville & Mowbray	(021) 434 6167
Kalk Bay & Simons Town	(021) 761 1850
Plumstead	(082) 270 7392
Rondebosch	(021) 716 1850
Sea Point & Constantia	(082) 772 2122

Other
Chinese Martial Arts,
85 Station Road, Observatory
Tel: (021) 448 2594

International Taijiquan & Saolin Wushu
Association
Tel: (021) 439 1373

Kushido School of Martial Arts,
32 Jameson Street, City bowl
Tel: (021) 423 7965

Kushido School of Martial Arts,
33 Mellville Road, Sea Scout Hall, Plumstead
Tel: (021) 797 58412

JKA Shotakan, Tai Chi (WU) Aikido,
1 Nerina Street, Milnerton
Tel: (021) 552 2721

Jing An Tai Chi Centre,
Gordon's Institute, Mowbray
Tel: (021) 671 0546

Tai Chi for Beginners,
52 Kloof Street, Gardens
& Jan van Riebeek School
Tel: (021) 586 32557

Durban
Tai Chi Chuan Institute of Health Centres
Bellair	(082) 772 8827
Berea	(082) 601 1841
Durban North	(082) 772 6627
La Lucia	(031) 368 1852

Other
Petron Valley Park Tai Chi School
Tel: (031) 705 4626

Gauteng
Tai Chi Institute of Health Centres
Killarney	(011) 786 6410
Mellville	(011) 726 2496
Rosebank	(011) 447 1649
Yeoville & Sandringham	(082) 856 6297
Zoo Lake & Midrand	(011) 482 4731

International Tai Chi Society Branches
Actonville	(083) 228 4888 / 421 0481
Auckland Park	(082) 855 2336 / 791 3183
Benoni	(011) 974 6253
Blairgowrie	(083) 625 9294 / 886 4318

Edenvale	(083) 757 2565 / 974 6253
Midrand	(011) 725 3894
Parkview, Sandown	(083)378 0468 / 782 2843
Wits University	(082) 469 5655 / 726 1070

Other
Rau Rau's Tai Chi School, Edenvale
Community Centre
Tel: (011) 804 5225

SA Tai Chi Federation
Tel: (011) 478 0836

Pietermaritzburg
Combat & Development Centre,
Clough Street
Tel: (033) 945 190

Judowaki Centre, 32 Clyde Street
Tel: (033) 455 796

Port Elizabeth
Elliot Martial Arts Academy,
William Moffett Elliot Centre:
Tel: (082) 565 464

Pretoria
Classical Martial Arts Centre,
8 St Alban's Scout Hall
Tel: (082) 600 7081

The Pretoria Tai Chi Federation
Tel: (012) 421 0498

Index